GEOLOGISTS' ASSOCIATION GUIDE No. 47

THE COASTAL LANDFORMS OF WEST DORSET

Edited by

Robert J. Allison

Department of Geological Sciences
University College London

Guides Editor: J.T. Greensmith

CONTENTS PAGE

PAGE

1. List of Tables

◆ ◆ ◆ ◆

2. List of Figures

PAGE

3. List of Grid References

Abbotsbury SY 577853

Beaminster ST 480015

Bindon SY 293898

Birdsmoorgate SY 392009

Black Down SY 613876

Black Ven SY 355929

Burton Bradstock SY 486896

Charmouth SY 366929

Chesil Beach SY 605810

Chesilton SY 683735

Chiswell SY 683735

Cockpit Hill ST 413012

Cogden Beach SY 504880

Coombpyne SY 290923

Coppett Hill SY 418958

Doghouse Hill SY 428913

Down Cliff SY 445912

East Cliff, Burton Bradstock SY 470900

Eggardon Hill SY 541946

Eype SY 448910

Eype Down SY 440923

Furzy Cliff SY 698817

Golden Cap SY 407923

Hardown Hill SY 405943

Higher Sea Lane SY 363930

Jan's Hill SY 426954

Lambert's Hill SY 371988

Langdon Hill SY 413932

Lyme Regis SY 343923

Old Lyme Road SY 348934

Osmington Mills SY 734816

Pilsdon Penn ST 405017

Pinhay Bay SY 320907

Portesham SY 603858

Portland Heights Hotel SY 691731

Portland Raised Beach SY 675684

Portland - Weymouth causeway SY 675750

Quarry Hill SY 434933

Seatown SY 420916

St Gabriel's Mouth SY 396923

Stonebarrow Hill SY 375927

Swyre SY 527883

The Cobb SY 338916

Thorncombe Beacon SY 435914

Vale of Marshwood SY 400970

Valley of the Stones SY 597876

Ware Cliffs SY 325910

West Bay SY 462904

West Bexington SY 532865

West Cliff, West Bay SY 452909

Weymouth SY 679795

Wyke Regis SY 660760

4. Access

Many of the sections in this guide include notes on access and a suggested route to be followed during site visits. The majority of the locations can be visited comfortably in half a day, although there is always scope for extending a visit. Longer visits allow a more leisurely pace to be taken along the routes described in the guide and this will almost inevitably increase enjoyment, as the time available for exploration and discovery is increased.

Public transport is available for access to a number of key locations. A regular British Rail service operates to Dorchester, Weymouth and Axminster, from where connections can be made with local bus services which operate along the coast. Bus services can be irregular. Users of the guide who will be relying on public transport are advised to check times and routes with the relevant operating authorities prior to departure. Details are also available in Tourist Information offices located in Weymouth, Dorchester and Lyme Regis.

The main A35(T) road has been considerably improved in recent years. Likewise, the B3157 coast road from Bridport to Weymouth will present no problems to the motorist. It is slower than the main trunkroad but the views along the coast on a clear day, particularly when travelling from west to east, are spectacular. A number of the minor roads down to the sea shore are narrow and in places care needs to be taken. The road to the summit of Stonebarrow Hill is a case in point. It is steep, narrow and has a number of sharp corners.

Access to most of the localities once away from roads is generally straightforward, either along the beach or along the Dorset Coast Footpath which runs throughout the area.

5. Accommodation

The west Dorset area has an abundant supply of hotels, guest houses and bed and breakfast accommodation. Within each category there is a considerable range of alternatives from quality full-board hotel accommodation on the one hand to self catering accommodation on the other. Further details are available from the English Tourist Board and local Tourist Information offices. Prior booking is advisable during busy holiday periods to avoid spending long periods of time locating suitable accommodation.

The Youth Hostel Association has two hostels in the area, one at Litton Cheney (SY 548900) and the other at Bridport (SY462930). Both hostels are heavily used and booking well in advance of proposed visits is strongly advised.

6. Unstable ground and personal safety

Visitors to many of the sites described in this Guide must take particular care to avoid accident and injury. Most of the localities to be visited combine the two most common causes of accident and injury, namely unstable cliffs and wave and tide hazards. Fatalities are recorded every year.

If treated with respect, the moving cliffs of west Dorset are not dangerous. A number of basic guidelines should be followed at all times.

1. Do not visit sites of unstable ground alone, particularly during the winter months or after prolonged periods of heavy rainfall.

2. Always wear walking boots or stout lace-up shoes. Wellington boots are not recommended.

3. Do not attempt to traverse ground which is very wet or appears to be water logged.

4. If the ground becomes increasingly soft and muddy turn back. Do not adopt the attitude that it is better to press on regardless.

5. Keep clear of overhangs and steep exposures. Blocks of rock often become detached in a random manner and it is almost impossible to predict where the next fall will occur. Hard hats are essential when working close to steep cliffs.

6. Do not climb the cliffs. They are friable and likely to collapse under the extra weight.

7. If you do begin to sink into the mud do not struggle or panic. Rapid movements with the feet and legs in an attempt to free oneself do more harm than good. In such a situation, slowly pull one foot out of the ground. If necessary sit, or lie down on the ground surface and, in a similar manner, slowly pull the second foot until it is free. It is inevitable in such a situation that you will get muddy but by increasing the amount of contact you have with the ground and spreading body weight, you will eliminate the likelihood of becoming stuck fast.

Before visiting any site where access necessitates walking along a beach, study the local tide tables. The high tides at Portland Bill are usually noted in local newspapers and tide tables for the surrounding area can be purchased locally. The Admiralty Tide Tables, published annually, are the primary source of information. Tides at Lyme Regis are approximately 30 minutes earlier than they are at Portland Bill.

Do not walk to outcrops or exposures at the foot of coastal cliffs on a rising tide. Many of the beaches along the west Dorset coast shelve very steeply and swimming in the sea is dangerous. There is a strong under-tow along much of the coast and large waves have sufficient power to sweep even the strongest of swimmers out to sea. If in doubt contact the Coastguard before venturing along the shore line.

7. Weather

Although severe storm conditions are rare along the west Dorset coast, high winds and heavy rain can make conditions very difficult. Sites where access involves walking along a beach should not be visited during storms or during rough seas. In windy conditions routes along the tops of the coastal cliffs should be avoided. There are some steep, near vertical drops and wind patterns close to the edge of cliffs can be erratic and unpredictable.

Conversely, during hot, sunny weather, sunburn and dehydration are a risk due to reflection of sunlight from the surface of the sea.

8. Maps

Dorset has excellent map coverage with the 1 : 50,000 and 1 : 25,000 Ordnance Survey sheets showing public rights of way. The Grid References used in this Guide are most easily located on the Ordnance Survey 1 : 50,000 Landranger Series.

The west Dorset coast is covered by the following 1 : 50,000 Ordnance Survey Landranger series maps.

1. Sheet 193: Taunton and Lyme Regis.
2. Sheet 194: Dorchester and Weymouth.

The area is also covered by the following 1 : 25,000 Ordnance Survey maps of the Pathfinder series or Second series.

1. Sheet SY 29/39: Lyme Regis and Axminster.
2. Sheet SY 49/59: Bridport.
3. Sheet SY 58: Abbotsbury.
4. Sheet SY 68/78: Weymouth (North).
5. Sheet SY 67/77: Weymouth and Portland.

The following British Geological Survey map sheets are available at a scale of 1 : 50,000 or, in the older editions, at a scale of one inch to the mile.

1.	Sheet 326/340:	Sidmouth and Lyme Regis.
2.	Sheet 327:	Bridport.
3.	Sheet 328:	Dorchester.
4.	Sheet 341/342:	West Fleet and Weymouth.

9. Acknowledgements

Thanks are due to a number of people who have contributed to the production of this Guide. The figures have been drawn by the ever skilful and patient hand of Colin Stuart and the plates have been efficiently produced by Mike Gray; both are in the Department of Geological Sciences at University College London. Trevor Greensmith made helpful comments on manuscript. A succession of doctoral research projects have provided much of the background for many of the individual contributions. Collective, but by no means diminished thanks, goes to all involved in these earlier feats of academic achievement.

Finally, all the contributors to the Guide have been inspired, to some greater or lesser degree, by Denys Brunsden. His enthusiasm for the coastal cliffs of Dorset is infectious. His energy and encouragement have rubbed off onto us all.

INTRODUCTION

Robert J. Allison

Geomorphological perspectives

This field guide has its origins in a recent field meeting convened by the editor on behalf of the British Geomorphological Research Group (BGRG). The principal aim of the meeting was to examine the processes which dominate the coastal cliffs of west Dorset and the resulting landforms. Parts of this guide, now substantially modified in content, were included in an accompanying field book for the BGRG meeting. Much new material has since been added in the production of this publication.

The Dorset coast has many sites of key geomorphological importance in the British Isles, which are frequently the subject of field investigation by geologists and geographers. Indeed as Brunsden and Goudie (1981) note, the Dorset coast is one of the most beautiful and spectacular coastlines in the

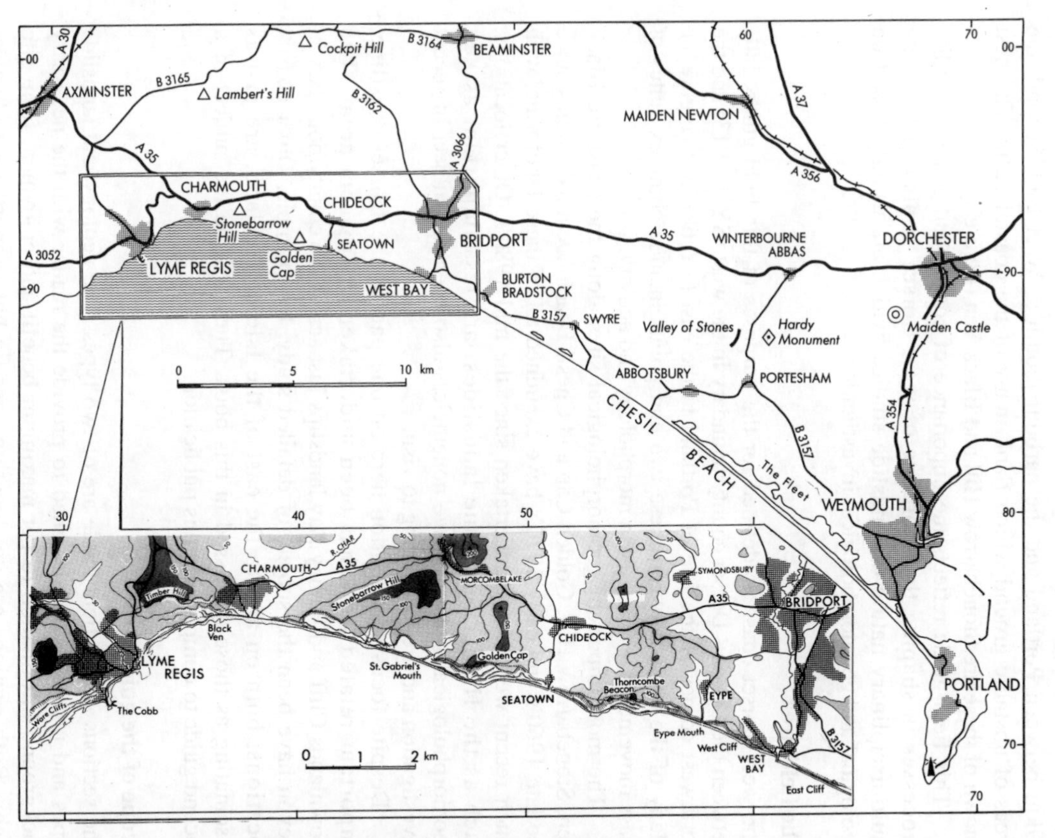

Figure 1. Major topographic characteristics of the Dorset coast.

world, comprising sites of remarkable scientific importance. The shoreline between the Isle of Portland and Lyme Regis is best known for two things. First, the imposing shingle ridge of Chesil Beach, which extends for some 29km between Portland and the harbour mouth at West Bay. Second, the areas of unstable ground which flank many of the coastal cliffs. The best known of these are Stonebarrow Hill and Black Ven (Figure 1).

This field guide reflects the importance of coastal and slope instability processes in shaping the shoreline of west Dorset. It also reflects the multidisciplinary nature of landslide studies, which are usually based on geological and geomorphological investigations.

The field area

The west Dorset coast, as defined for the purposes of this field guide, falls between the Devon - Dorset county boundary in the west (SY 332913) and the northwest corner of the Isle of Portland in the east (SY 683736) (Figure 1). Many of the cliffs between these two end points include complex suites of mass movements which vary in morphology and activity.

The most important geomorphological sites along the coast are Black Ven, Stonebarrow Hill, Golden Cap and Chesil Beach. Detailed studies since the late 1960's and early 1970's have examined all of these landforms, with much recent work being undertaken since the mid 1980's. Other locations, such as the Higher Sea Lane landslides, are less important as key geomorphological sites but have nonetheless also been the subject of recent investigation and are fascinating to visit.

Despite focusing attention here on one part of the Dorset coastline, important related work has been undertaken in adjacent areas. The Downlands Cliff and Pinhay Bay landslips just across the county boundary in Devon have been the subject of detailed study, for example. Other coastal locations, both on and to the east of the Isle of Portland, are just as fascinating as those discussed in this book. They will be the subject of a second guide to complement this publication.

Scope of the guide

The sections in this field guide are of two types. The geology and landslide types and processes are designed to provide the reader with the necessary background information to get maximum benefit and enjoyment from site visits. Both sections are not location specific but support other chapters where site itineraries are provided. The important geological characteristics of west Dorset focus on the lithological and structural controls on cliff stability. Knowledge of the main geological units in the region is essential for considering the geomorphology. However, this guide provides no more than a geological summary. For a more detailed description reference should be made to House (1989), also available from the Geologists' Association.

The remaining sections include notes on access and suggested routes for examining key sites in the area. The majority of these are at the coast and focus on present day processes but one chapter reviews important aspects of the region's denudational past in an attempt to summarise the complex tertiary history of the area. A number of attempts have been made to reconstruct former land surfaces as a starting point for examining present day geomorphological processes; all are fraught with uncertainty due to fragmentary evidence.

With the high level of interest that exists in this part of the British coastline, it is inevitable that many other publications and guides are available to those wishing to discover more about the area. The text is widely referenced and all relevant publications are listed in a comprehensive bibliography at the end of this guide. The Geologists' Association publishes an excellent guide to the Geology of the Dorset coast (House, 1989). There are a number of British Geological Survey memoirs, the most recent of which (Melville and Freshney, 1982) provides an overview of the geology of the west Dorset coastline. There are also a variety of other specialist guides including a detailed discussion of the Jurassic sequence in Dorset (Torrens, 1969), a guide for petroleum geologists (Stoneley and Selley, 1986) and a less comprehensive geomorphological field booklet (Brunsden and Goudie, 1981).

GEOLOGY

Robert J. Allison

Introduction

The coastal cliffs of west Dorset provide one of the best locations in the British Isles to study rocks of Jurassic and Cretaceous age (Ager and Smith, 1965) (Figure 2). Exposures on steep, seaward facing slopes are almost continuous, providing classic lithological sections. Nowhere is the interaction between lithology, earth surface processes and the resulting landforms so clearly seen (House, 1989).

Complex folds and faults are almost completely absent (Chatwin, 1960; Melville and Freshney, 1982) and the lack of structural controls enhances the ease with which associations can be drawn between geology and geomorphology. The Jurassic rocks include Liassic, Middle Jurassic and Upper Jurassic sediments. To the west of Weymouth the Lias rocks have a predominant silt and clay matrix, display gentle east-southeasterly dips of around 2° to 3° and are overlain unconformably by Lower Cretaceous sediments.

A brief summary of the main geological units of the region (Table 1) provides an ideal base-line for considering the associations between geology, geomorphology and coastal landslides.

Stratigraphy - the Jurassic sequence

The oldest Jurassic rocks exposed along the west Dorset coast are the Lias (Lower Jurassic) (Figure 3), comprising thinly bedded alternations of marls, clays and limestones, beds of shale, layers of cementstone and beds of sand and sandstone (Lang, 1936; Lang et al., 1926, 1928; Palmer, 1972). Liassic sediments form the largest part of all outcrops throughout the region and sections in the coastal cliffs reach 200m in thickness. Their outcrop passes inland and stretches in a broad tract northwards almost to Beaminster (ST 480015) and into the area known as the Vale of Marshwood (SY 400970).

Fossils are common. Assemblages indicate shallow, near-shore marine environments, suggesting that at the time of deposition much of the present land surface of England was under the sea (Hallam, 1964). The nearest ancient land mass to the west during the Lower Jurassic comprised Cornwall and part of Devon. The present Mendips were the site of islands and shallow water shoals and tracts of land were also exposed stretching from East Anglia to London and Kent. Rivers flowing across these land surfaces discharged into the shallow seas. Since then, the stratified sediments have been subject to chemical and physical changes, resulting in the rock units seen today, exhibiting varying degrees of resistance to weathering and erosion.

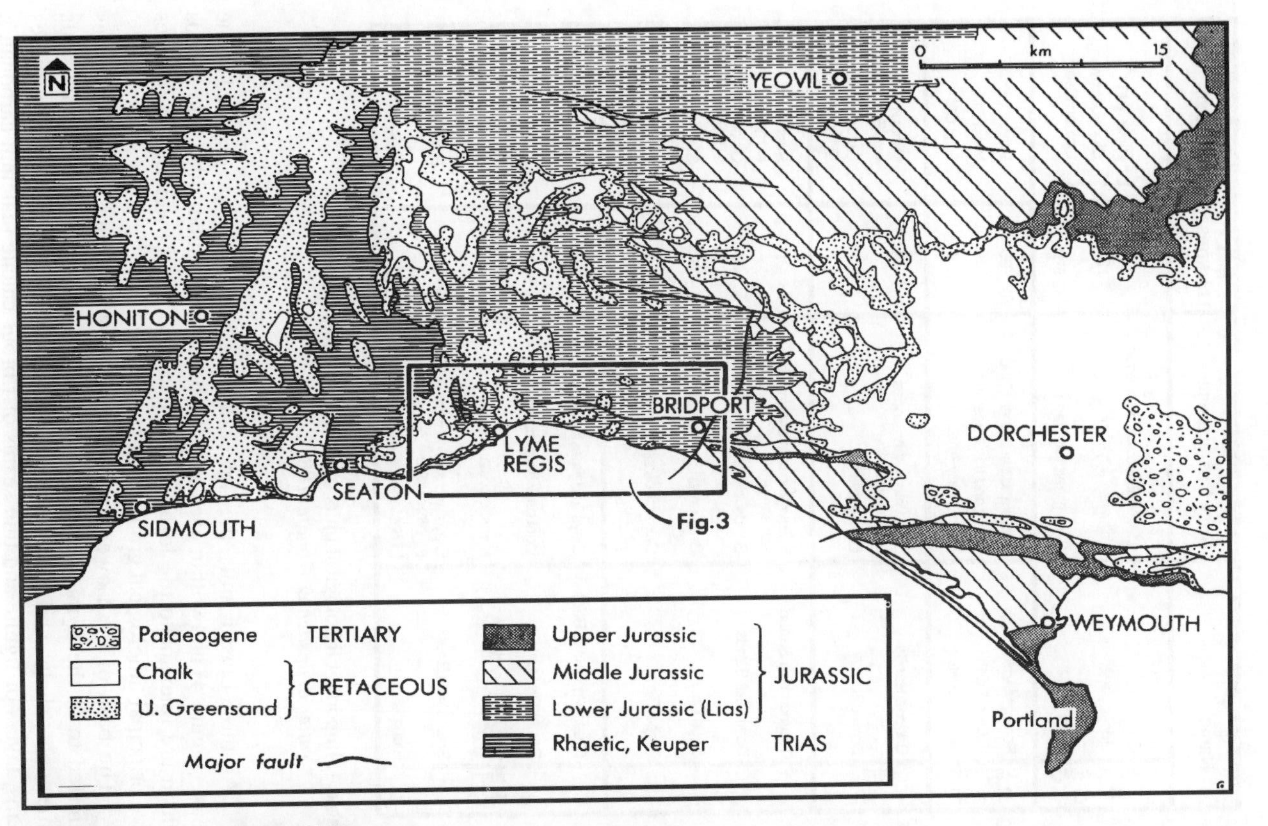

Figure 2. Geology of the west Dorset coast.

	Name	Rock Characteristic	Max Thickness (metres)	Outcrop
Lower Cretaceous	Chert	Close-jointed, hard siliceous	9	Black Ven
	Upper Greensand	Yellowish silty-sand	30	Stonebarrow
	Gault	Grey-green silty-sand	5-15	Golden Cap
Middle Jurassic	Forest Marble	Clays and shelly limestone	25	West Cliff
	Fuller's Earth	Clays and thin limestone	45	West Cliff
	Inferior Oolite	Hard, shelly limestone	6	East Cliff
Upper Lias	Bridport Sands	Soft, yellow sandstones, some hard bands	49	Various locations e.g. East Cliff
	Downcliff Clay	Blue-grey clay	21	Golden Cliff to Eype Mouth
Middle Lias	Thorncombe Sands	Yellow and light brown soft sands	21	Seaton to Eype
	Down Cliff Sands	Sands, clays and marls	30	Golden Cap to Eype
	Eype Clay	Grey-green hard sandstone	60	Stonebarrow to West Cliff
	Three Tiers	Calcareous silty sandstone	9	Stonebarrow to Seaton
Lower Lias	Green Ammonite Beds	Clays and limestones	32	Black Ven to Seaton
	Belemnite Marls	Light grey hard mudstone	23	Black Ven to Golden Cap
	Black Ven Marls	Marls, clays and shales	46	Stonebarrow to Black Ven
	Shales with Beef	Clays and shales with thin limestone	21	Black Ven
	Blue Lias	Limestones, shales and marls	32	Black Ven

Table 1. Important lithological units of the west Dorset coast *(after Brunsden & Goudie, 1981)*.

All three Liassic units, the Lower, Middle and Upper, are exposed at the coast (Figure 4) and within each unit the beds can be subdivided into groups which are relevant to the local geomorphology. The Lower Lias comprises five principal lithological groups (Table 1).

The base of the Lower Lias is marked by the Blue Lias, sometimes referred to as the Lyme Regis Beds. The Blue Lias comprises argillaceous limestones, shales and marls with occasional and finely divided iron pyrites veins, layers of lignite and thin seams of fibrous calcite (calcium carbonate),

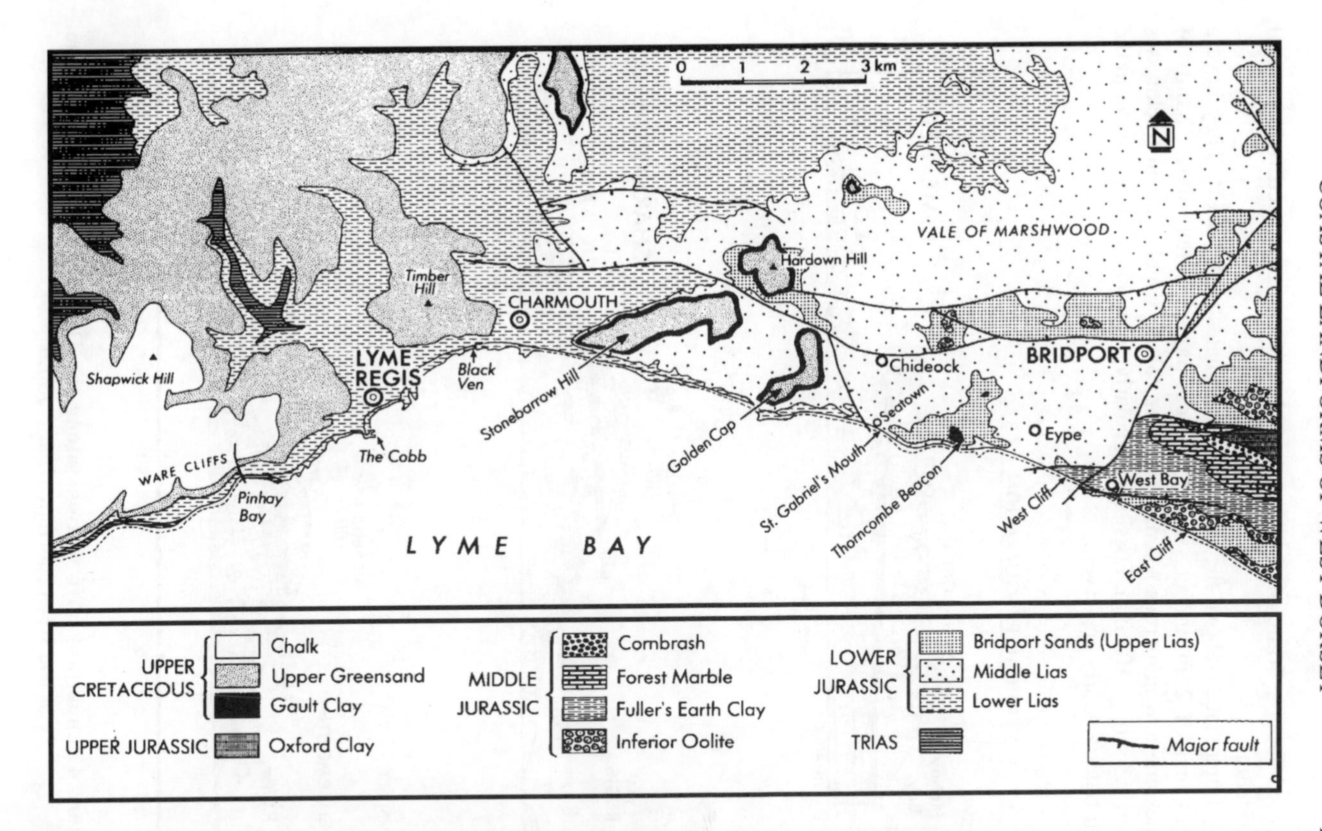

Figure 3. Geology of the area between Lyme Regis and Weymouth.

termed 'beef'. Some of the limestone bands can be traced over several kilometres.

Immediately above the Blue Lias are Shales with 'Beef'. They have a thickness of 25m and consist of shales, paper shales, marls, bands of limestone and numerous seams of fibrous calcite which vary in thicknesses from 1.5 mm to 102 mm. Fossils, particularly ammonites, are common in the unit but are poorly preserved.

VERTICAL EXAGGERATION X3

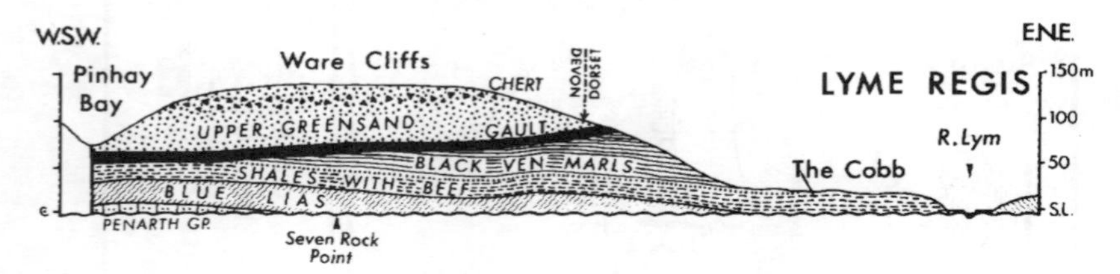

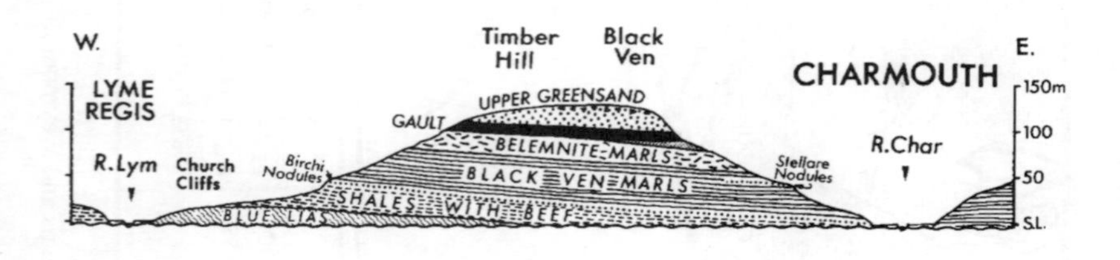

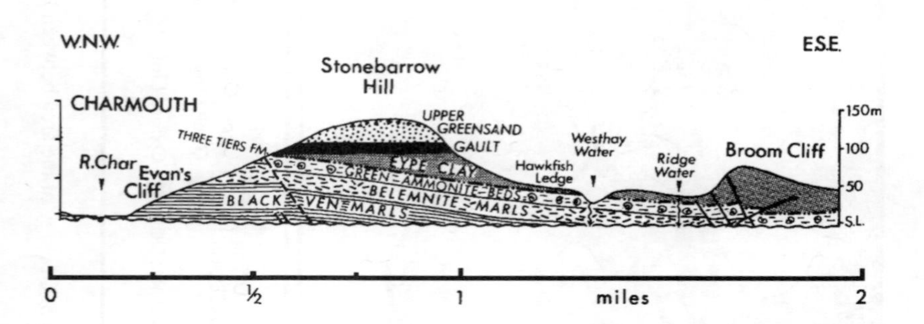

Figure 4. Important cliff sections along the Dorset coast between Lyme Regis and Weymouth *(after House, 1989)*.

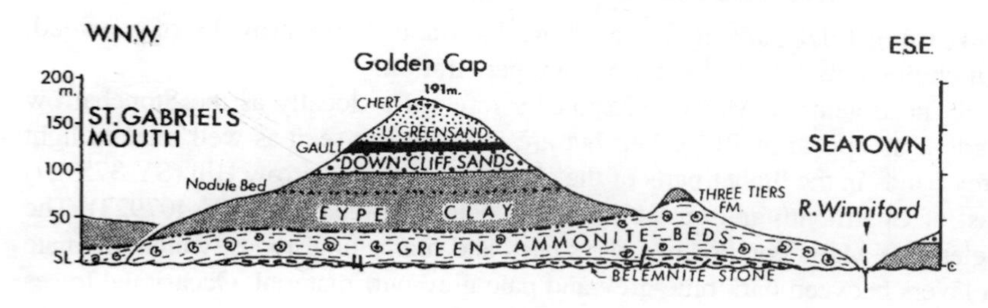

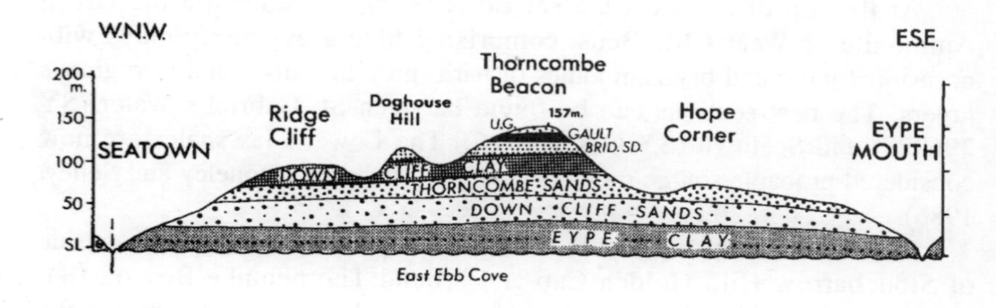

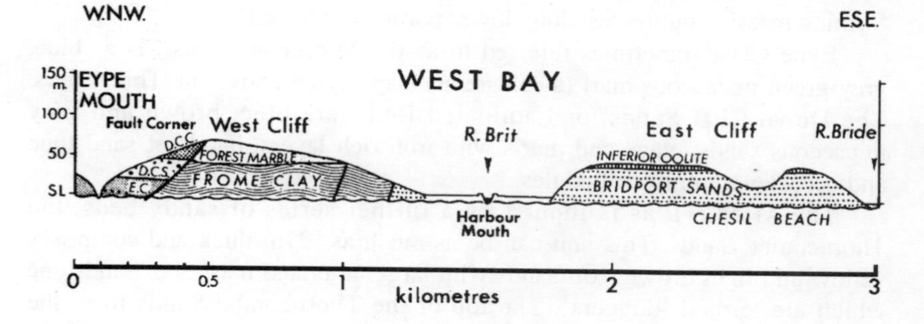

Figure 4. Continued

Black Ven Marls, as the name suggests, are clearly seen in the cliffs of Black Ven (SY 355929) east of Lyme Regis (Figure 4). They are a more purely argillaceous deposit than the adjacent sediments, comprising dark shales, marls and clays with thin non-continuous limestone and cementstone bands. The Black Ven Marls yield magnificently preserved ammonites and are thought to have been deposited in shallow lagoons, sheltered from waves and strong tidal currents by offshore bars and dense growths of seaweed, which prevented daylight and oxygen penetration.

The Belemnite Marls, occasionally referred to locally as the Stonebarrow Beds, also appear at Black Ven but are most clearly seen as well marked light grey bands in the higher parts of the clay cliffs at Stonebarrow Hill (SY 375927) east of Charmouth and on the foreshore below Golden Cap (SY 407923). The Belemnite Marls comprise marls, shales and marly limestones, which alternate in layers between dark blue-grey and pale grey-buff material. Occasional traces of iron pyrites and lignite are present. Belemnites abound both in the marl and in the thin limestone band which marks the upper limit of the unit.

At the top of the west Dorset Lower Lias sequence are the Green Ammonite or Wear Cliff Beds, comprising blue-grey marly clays with occasional indurated bands, nodules of hard grey limestone and ferruginous layers. The best sections can be found between St. Gabriel's Water (SY 396923) and Seatown (SY G.R.420916). The Lower Lias shales are now considered probable source rocks for local oil seepages (Stoneley and Selley, 1986).

Excellent outcrops of Middle Lias sediments can be seen at the east side of Stonebarrow Hill, Golden Cap and around Thorncombe Beacon (SY 435914). The Middle Lias comprises four principal groups. At the base is the Three Tiers Formation, composed of three thick, calcareous sandstone bands. The unit stands out clearly above the Green Ammonite Beds at Golden Cap, forming massive buttresses along lower portions of the cliff.

Eype Clay, sometimes referred to as the Micaceous Beds, is a blue, grey-green micaceous marl (a calcareous clay), lying above the Three Tiers. The Down Cliff Sands, or Laminated Beds, are blue, brown and grey micaceous sands, clays and marls with iron rich layers, bands of sandstone and occasional ironstone nodules.

The Middle Lias is topped by a further series of sandy beds, the Thorncombe Sands. This unit can be as much as 27m thick and comprises yellow and light brown, soft sands with large indurated masses of sandstone which are termed 'doggers'. The top of the Thorncombe Sands form the junction between the Middle and Upper Lias. The junction is beautifully exposed in a number of places including the top of Down Cliff (SY 445912) and the face of Thorncombe Beacon. It is highlighted by a fossiliferous band which displays evidence of marine erosion.

The gradual upwards progression from micaceous silty clays to sands and finally limestones within the Middle Lias succession indicates a progressive shallowing of the sea during deposition. The marine transgression continued in Upper Liassic times. Two units of the Upper Lias are relevant here. Down Cliff Clay is the lower unit and comprises 21 m of blue-grey clay, which becomes increasingly sandy towards the top. Resting on top of the Down Cliff Clay is the upper unit formed of shoal- and storm-deposited sands known as the Bridport Sands. This unit forms stunning cliffs on the eastern side of West Bay Harbour. The material is a bright yellow, soft sandstone, with more resistant bands of indurated but crumbly sandstone and sandy limestone (Davies, 1967, 1969). In addition to the Upper Lias, three Middle Jurassic units also crop out in cliff sections. The Bridport Sands pass up through sandy limestones into the Inferior Oolite (3m to 6m), which varies considerably in lithology but is predominantly a hard, shelly limestone, containing some noticeable sandy units (Richardson, 1928; Parsons, 1976). The best sections can be examined in East Cliff, near to Burton Bradstock (SY 470900). Two Great Oolite units are also present, outcropping beyond Thorncombe Beacon. They are most clearly exposed at West Cliff (SY 452909). The succeeding Fuller's Earth Clay is a sequence of interbedded clays and shelly limestones, followed by the Forest Marble which is a hard, flaggy limestone, yellow in colour with green-brown clay bands both above and below the main flaggy limestone unit.

Stratigraphy - the Cretaceous sequence

The remaining rock units outcropping along the west Dorset coast are of Cretaceous age. They include the Gault and Upper Greensand.

Between Lyme Regis and Weymouth the Cretaceous sediments occur as capping deposits at topographic highs such as Black Ven (SY 355929), Stonebarrow Hill (SY 375927) and Golden Cap (SY 407923) (Figure 4). Three units are present: Gault, Upper Greensand and Chert Beds. The Gault and Upper Greensand are sometimes regarded as variations of one formation in this region, the former being a more clayey deposit and the latter a sandy facies (Wilson et al., 1958). The Gault rests unconformably on the Middle Lias at Golden Cap, the Middle and Lower Lias at Stonebarrow and the Lower Lias at Black Ven. It is characteristically a silty-clayey, glauconitic, grey-green deposit (Table 1), with a basal conglomerate. The Upper Greensand lies above the Gault and, although being very similar in character, is more a yellow-orange, silty and fine grained sand and contains layers of Chert nodules. One locally important component of the Greensand is sometimes referred to as 'Foxmould'. This brown and grey sandy facies is increasingly loamy towards its base and is occasionally subject to liquefaction.

Structure

Until recently, the broad structural characteristics of central southern England were thought to be easy to interpret (Chatwin, 1960) and it was assumed that structural deformations were mainly concurrent with the Alpine uplift (or orogeny) Dorset appears to have been at the margin of the Alpine mountain building region and this resulted in the development of east-west trending 'ripple', 'crest' and 'trough' structures. Recent evidence (Melville and Freshney, 1982) suggests that the situation is somewhat more complex than in the original interpretations. Asymmetric folds are thought to be due to the draping of plastic Mesozoic and Tertiary strata over active basement faults, thus relating the structures to tensional movements. The movement history of east-west faults is indeed complex, in some cases involving direction reversals. Other faults trend north-west to south-east and are now thought to be related to a steep gravity gradient trending north-west to south-east and representing a deep-seated structural line cutting basement rocks (Figure 5).

The coastal cliffs immediately to the east of Lyme Regis are remarkable for their lack of structural complexity. Strata are almost horizontally bedded, dipping between 2° and 3° east-southeast. The Jurassic sequence is capped by unconformable Cretaceous sediments but only minor folds and faults interrupt almost continuous exposures along the coast (House, 1989).

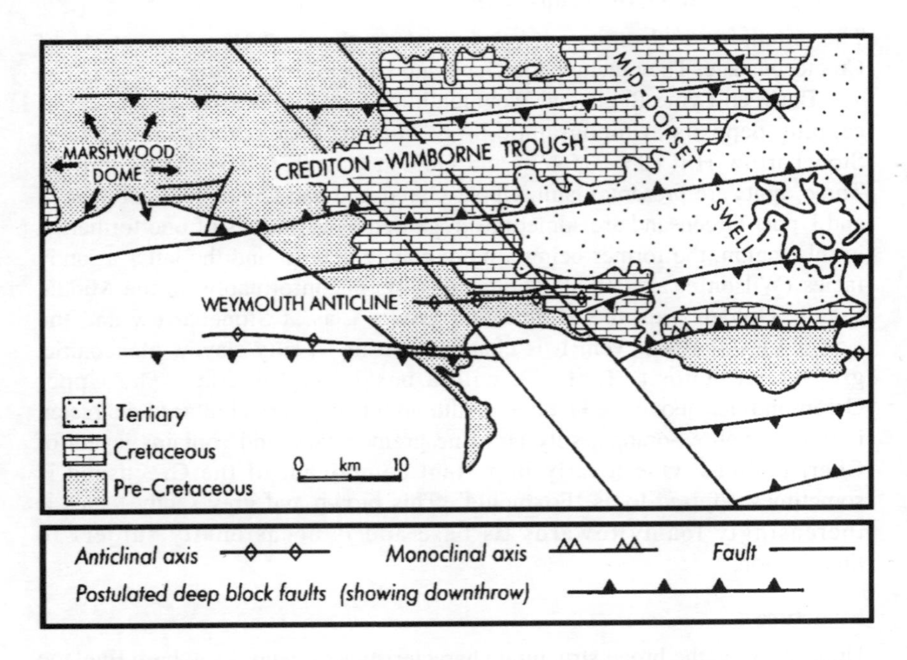

Figure 5. Structural characteristics of the Dorset coast *(after Melville & Freshney, 1982)*.

In contrast, in east Dorset the situation is somewhat more complex, with the presence of the Weymouth Anticline and Purbeck Monocline. The Weymouth Anticline is a broad arch of Jurassic rocks, with its asymmetry due to a more steeply dipping northerly limb. While the northern limb of the Weymouth Anticline is thought to be pre-Gault / Upper Greensand, the offshore geology around the Isle of Portland suggests that the more gently dipping southerly limb is at least partly younger and Tertiary in age, linking in with the Purbeck Monocline. The Isle of Portland is the remnant of the southerly limb of the Weymouth anticline, as shown by the gentle southward dip of the beds.

The structure of the beds plays an important role in cliff instability and landslide activity. For example, around Black Ven and Stonebarrow Hill it is the unconformable nature of the permeable Cretaceous sediments above the low permeability clays and shales of the Lias which accounts for much of the landslide activity.

Summary

The geology of the west Dorset coast is well documented and excellently summarised by House (1989). The discussion presented here is a summary of the key points which have to be considered in a discussion of the coastal landforms. The stratigraphy and structure hold important implications for both the overall geomorphology of the area and in particular for the stability of coastal cliffs.

Two key points must be borne in mind. First, the juxtaposition of different stratigraphic units of varying lithological character has an important control on landslide behaviour. Second, structural controls are significant. These include regional controls on the one hand and the local consequence of regional influences, such as changes to the dip of bedding and the juxtaposition of rock units of different character due to unconformities and faults, on the other.

DENUDATIONAL HISTORY

Clifford Embleton

Maps: Ordnance Survey 1:50,000 sheets 193, 194.
Ordnance Survey 1:25,000 sheets SY29/39, SY49/59, SY58, ST20/30.
British Geological Survey 1:50,000 sheet 327.

Introduction

Golden Cap (SY 407923), the highest sea cliff in southern England, rises to 191m. From its summit on a clear day, the view extends from the Isle of Portland in the east to the coast of Devon and Start Point in the west. Inland, the view takes in a dissected landscape of low hills and ridges, many of them flat-topped, drained by the River Brit in the east entering the sea at West Bay, the Char leading to Charmouth and, in the west, the Lim at Lyme Regis. Between Lyme Regis and Bridport, the higher coastal hills mostly rise to between 150 and 200m. The highest, Hardown Hill (SY 405943), touches 207m.

The flat-topped hills are generally capped with near-horizontal Albian beds (Gault, Upper Greensand, Chert Beds); their flanks slope steeply at 25° to 35° before flattening out in gentler foot slopes of about 10° developed in the underlying Lias clays and leading down to the valley floors.

The Albian rests unconformably on the Lias. Its base can be found at a height of about 120m in Golden Cap, rising northwards to about 135m in Hardown Hill and 150m in Coppet Hill (SY 418958) (summit 161m) (Figure 6). To the east in Thorncombe Beacon (summit 157m) the sub-Albian unconformity stands at 145m but west of Golden Cap it descends slowly to about 100m in Stonebarrow (cliff-top summit 157m) and remains at that height around Lyme Regis. The surface of the unconformity is thus gently warped, and a downward flexure corresponds to the position of the Char valley. Some hills have lost their Albian capping through slope retreat but still rise to about the level of the sub-Albian unconformity (Quarry Hill (SY 434933), Jan's Hill (SY 426954), for example). Eype Down (155m) (SY 440923) has a minute outlier of Gault only.

Five to six kilometres north of Golden Cap lies the centre of the Vale of Marshwood (Figure 6), a roughly oval-shaped lowland whose floor drops to about 50m to 60m, drained by the Char and its tributaries. Structurally it is an unroofed elongated dome of Jurassic rocks, in the core of which denudation has exposed the Lower Lias. In this area no trace of the former Albian cover has survived. Denudation has cut away the Lias to depths of 100m or more

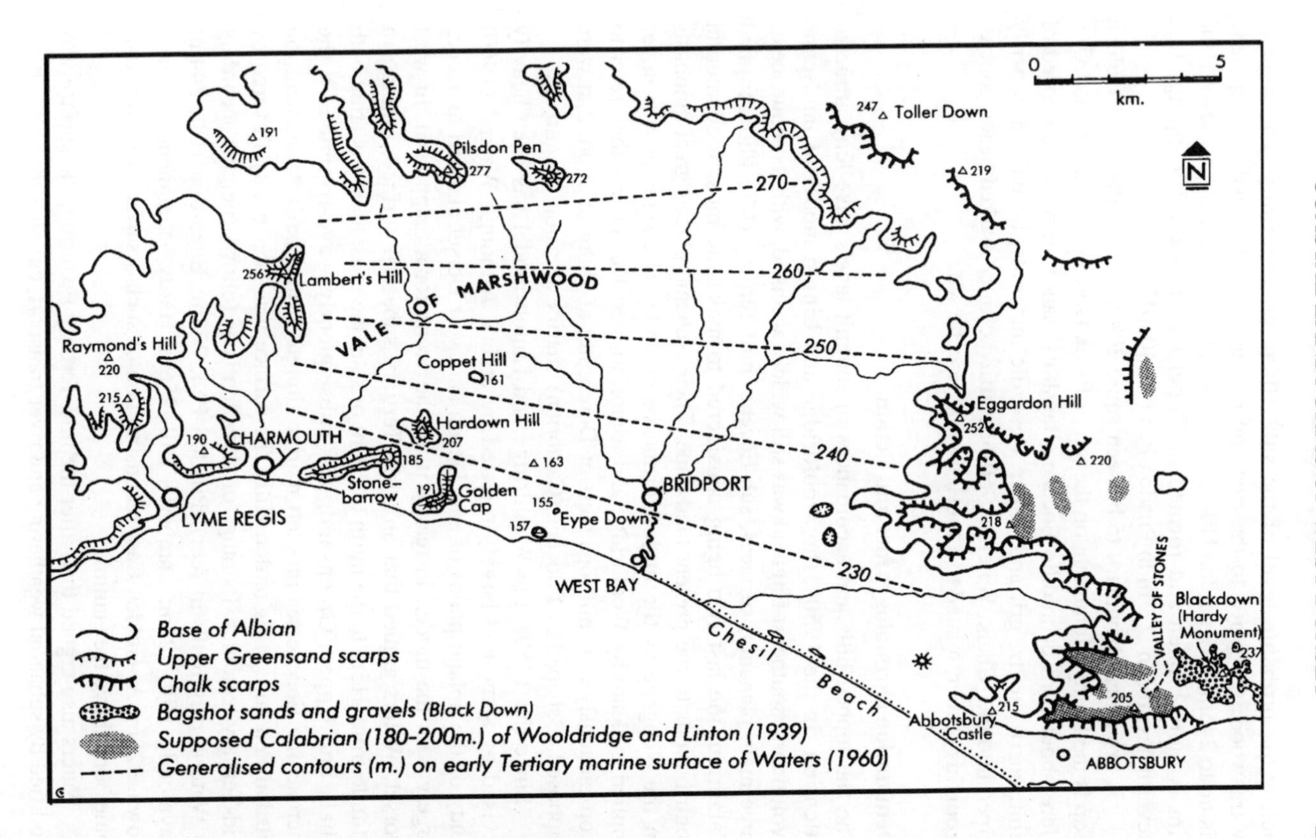

Figure 6. Some topographic and geological features of West Dorset.

below the probable level of the sub-Albian unconformity. The Vale of Marshwood is rimmed to the east and northeast by the Chalk escarpment, rising to 245m in Eggardon Hill (SY 540946). On the west and northwest, the rim is more broken and formed of Upper Greensand hill cappings that nevertheless reach 277m in Pilsdon Pen (ST 405017).

A prominent landmark to be seen some 20km east-south/east of Golden Cap is the Hardy Monument on the top of Black Down (SY 613876) at 237m. Here about 10m of middle Eocene (Bagshot) sandy gravels, composed of flint, chert, quartz, grit and other Mesozoic materials, lie on and is partly piped into the Chalk. Waters (1960) identified chatter-marked beach cobbles from this outlier, related to a transgressing Eocene sea.

Denudation chronology: fact and fiction

The flat topped hills and accordances in summit levels have long attracted attention. In the 1950s, the Wooldridge and Linton model of landscape evolution in southeast England was still widely accepted, with its sequence of three main planation surfaces, sub-Eocene, mid-Tertiary (Mio-Pliocene) and Calabrian, the last two being considered to make the most fundamental contributions to the present landscape. Their scheme placed great emphasis on the Neogene as the major formative episode. The scheme was never applied in detail by Wooldridge and Linton to west Dorset, but they refer to 'conspicuously flat' hill tops west of Dorchester at 180m to 200m that were supposedly `shaped by Pliocene (Calabrian) marine abrasion' (Figure 6).

Since the 1950s, the Wooldridge and Linton model has been heavily revised by some and largely rejected by others. Although Waters' (1960) study of the upland plains of east Devon and west Dorset claimed to accord largely with the model, in reality it set the scene for a reappraisal. In west Dorset, Waters argued that an early Tertiary subaerial surface, ranging in altitude from 315m to the north to 200m or so at the coast and truncating both Chalk and Upper Greensand, was subsequently wave-trimmed by the encroaching Eocene sea that left marine shingle at the Hardy Monument, on Pilsdon Pen and on Eggardon Hill. The surface was later gently flexured by mid-Tertiary tectonics. Its range of elevation is as follows (heights according to Waters, originally in feet): Pilsdon Pen, 277m; Eggardon Hill, 244m; Raymond's Hill, 221m; Lambert's Hill, 256m; Hardy Monument on Black Down, 229m. At Golden Cap, reconstruction of such a surface would take it some 30m above the summit.

Waters also argued that, after the mid-Tertiary flexuring, the surface was modified by subaerial weathering and river transport, culminating in a further phase of planation in the Neogene. The final form of the surface, which Waters compared with the Mio-Pliocene surface of Wooldridge and Linton, was said to differ only slightly from the early Tertiary marine-trimmed surface. Extending from Dartmoor to Wessex, it bears not only relics of early Eocene weathering and mid-Eocene marine action, but further residues from Oligocene and Neogene weathering, yielding altogether a rubble of chert, flint and sarsens, including both angular fragments and rounded cobbles, in a sandy and clayey matrix. This is the detritus that has variously been labelled plateau drift, pebbly clay and sand and clay-with-flints. There is clear evidence that in the Pleistocene, it suffered considerable disturbance through cryoturbation, frost shattering of clasts and gelifluction on slopes.

An early Tertiary surface was also identified in adjacent areas of Wiltshire (Green, 1969) and Wessex (Green, 1974). In Wessex, Green distinguished two closely spaced surfaces both of Neogene age: a higher, Miocene surface (c.180m to 260m) and a lower one of Pliocene age (c. 140m to 240m), whose planation all but destroyed any trace of the Palaeogene land surface (260m). The range of altitudes of these Neogene surfaces was ascribed to late Pliocene to early Pleistocene tectonic deformation. Green (1985) also invoked differential uplift to explain differences in elevation of Cretaceous and Palaeogene sediments in southwest England and a hypothesis of neotectonic fault-block displacement was extended by implication to areas farther east. Green found no evidence for any Calabrian marine transgression.

In the last decade the opinion has gradually been gaining acceptance that the main formative phase in the evolution of southern England was not the Neogene, as originally suggested by Wooldridge and Linton, but Palaeogene. The basis for such a view has come from a fundamental reassessment of both the sedimentary and the geomorphological evidence. The arguments are set out in detail by Jones (1980, 1981), Small (1980) and Green (1985). In brief, it is argued that a long-continued phase of Palaeogene subaerial weathering and denudation was punctuated by shorter intervals of marine transgression, such as deposited the Bagshot cobbles at the Hardy Monument and was accompanied by low-key tectonic deformation. The 'sub-Palaeogene surface' is thus polygenetic and variably deformed; it is demonstrably time-transgressive and its formation spanned 17-27 million years as shown by the stratigraphic relationships of the overlying deposits. By late Palaeogene times, it seems probable that most of southern England comprised a surface of low relief close to base level; it is thus easy to understand why the volume of Oligocene terrigenous sediment in southern England is so small (Green, 1985).

The clay-with-flints

The various Palaeogene sediments have been largely stripped away from the Chalk uplands in Dorset. Beneath the thinning and disintegrating Palaeogene cover, the clay-with-flints *sensu stricto* formed by chalk solution (more actively, perhaps, in the warmer Palaeogene phases but continuing throughout the Tertiary) and by incorporation of Palaeogene residues. It has not yet been clearly identified in south Dorset, partly because of Pleistocene disturbance and mixing.

The evidence of sarsens

Duricrusts of siliceous material up to 5m thick also developed during warm phases with seasonal rainfall in host materials of Palaeocene-Eocene age, the silicification taking place especially in the more tectonically stable Oligocene. At this time, as already mentioned, a surface of low relief (now standing at about 250m to 300m) may have extended across Dorset. The silcrete formed either at the surface or within the weathering profile (Summerfield and Goudie, 1980). Later, in the Neogene, climatic and tectonic changes inhibited its formation and its disintegration yielded the sarsen stones such as are seen in the Valley of the Stones (SY 597876) just west of the Hardy Monument. No sarsens in Dorset are *in situ*; all have moved through natural agencies, such as Pleistocene solifluction, or by man. The fact that the sarsens now occur mostly in or on valley-floor sediments suggests that perhaps the sheets of silcrete were never physically continuous over the whole area, for otherwise one would expect to find at least some remnants of such resistant material on the flat interfluves. It may be, as in the case of lateritic duricrusts in West Africa, that the duricrusts formed preferentially at the margins of shallow valleys crossing the surface.

Lateritic weathering profiles

Recent studies by Isaac (1979, 1981, 1983) have thrown further light on the residual upland deposits. Isaac's investigations are in Devon rather than Dorset, but one of his sites at Combpyne (SY 290923) lies only 24km west of Bridport. Some of the deposits of east Devon bear a superficial resemblance to the clay-with-flints of the Chalklands farther to the east and attain thicknesses locally up to 10m. Their accumulation and weathering characteristics reflect the 'establishment of a relatively stable land surface under an essentially tropical climate' (Isaac, 1983) dating from the early Palaeogene. A considerable thickness of Chalk was dissolved, so that in east Devon and west Dorset the deposits now rest largely on Upper Greensand. They include non-indurated kaolinitic and lateritic weathering profiles and silcretes yielding sarsens, witnessing a long and complex history of pedogenesis and diagenesis. The deposits in Devon appear to be older than the Oligocene Bovey Formation and the older profiles are dated as probably early Palaeocene. There is evidence of tectonic disturbance, including faulting, in the middle to upper Eocene, which appears to have initiated a phase of erosion of the deposits followed by the development of new weathering profiles. Erosion and sedimentation were accompanied by climatic change away from tropical conditions towards more temperate conditions through the Tertiary. Much later in the Quaternary, the residual deposits were subjected to further disturbance by periglacial action; some eolian material was also incorporated.

The residual deposits are not seen on Golden Cap but are clearly in evidence on Stonebarrow. Exposures in the main landslide scar show how variable they can be. In the centre of the scar, disturbed brick-red deposits may well prove to be lateritic / kaolinitic material of possibly Palaeogene age. If this is so, it is a striking indication of the stability of the flat hill-top surfaces over the last 60 million years.

Conclusion

South Dorset remains an area that is in need of further detailed investigation but evidence from surrounding areas has clear implications for it. On Golden Cap and Stonebarrow, the upper few metres of the cliff sections reveal the complexity of the residual deposits capping the Upper Greensand. They record, in highly compressed form, the 65 to 70 million years of complete dismantling of the former Chalk cover, which was here about 100m thick, the disintegration of the early Tertiary cover, the climatic and tectonic changes of the Cenozoic and the weathering response to these changes. The layers of angular and cryoturbated flint gravel bear witness not only to the destruction of the Chalk but also to the cold conditions of the Quaternary. Pockets and lenses of clay represent relics of weathering processes that may date back to the Palaeocene. Occasional rounded pebbles are to be found that may be derived from former marine Bagshot gravels that once capped the Chalk. This view seems now to be more credible than the view that they are Calabrian relics.

Reconstructions of former land surfaces have been attempted but are fraught with uncertainty because of the fragmentary evidence. The accordance of summit levels may be no more than an accident of long-continued denudation. On the other hand, it may be connected with one or more of the following: partial exhumation of the sub-Albian unconformity; the near-horizontal attitude of the Upper Greensand; exhumation of the sub-Palaeogene surface; wave trimming by the London Clay / Bagshot sea; minor modification in the Neogene; smoothing and summit lowering by periglacial activity in the Quaternary.

Access

A number of the sites are owned by the National Trust and all are well served by public footpaths. To get a clear view of the flat-topped hills and accordances in summit levels it is best to stand at one of the many topographic highs which abound throughout the area. Spectacular views, both inland and along the coast, await the visitor at a number of the localities. All are within a reasonable distance of each other but a vehicle is required for travel between the most interesting sites. Public transport is limited and would not be suitable for a day excursion for those wanting to visit a varied selection of places and achieve a full appreciation of the area's denudational history. The route described below comprises a sequence of drives between locations where car parking is available and short walks are required to reach the most suitable vantage points.

Individual taste can be used to produce variations on the suggestion noted below. Sites discussed above but not included in the route may be added, others omitted or longer visits made to a reduced selection of places. However, time should be spent at some, if not all, of the following: Cockpit Hill (ST 413012), Lambert's Hill (SY 371988),Golden Cap (SY 407923), Hardown Hill (SY 405943), the Valley of Stones (SY 597876) and Black Down (SY 613876).

Suggested Route

An approximately circular route can be taken, which initially skirts the Vale of Marshwood, then turns east and follows the coast to its conclusion at the Hardy Monument on the summit of Black Down (Figure 7).

Cockpit Hill (ST 413012) is immediately to the north of the B3164 road and provides an excellent starting point, with views south over the Vale of Marshwood towards the coast. In the east and northeast it is possible to pick out the rimming Chalk escarpment, while to the west and northwest, the rim is more broken and formed of Upper Greensand hill cappings. Car parking may be difficult but a short, steep footpath runs north from the B3164 road (SY 414010) to the summit triangulation point at an elevation of 277m.

Drive west along the B3164 road to the village of Birdsmoorgate (SY 392009) and from there south along the B3165 through Marshwood to Lambert's Hill (SY 371988). A car park is situated on the southern side of the road (SY 365988) which, at this point, forms the county boundary between Dorset and Devon. Public footpaths and tracks are clearly marked, passing on to National Trust land at the top of Lambert's Hill which includes a sequence of Archaeological earthworks. To the east the Vale of Marshwood unfolds while to the west the land drops away to the valley cut by the River Axe.

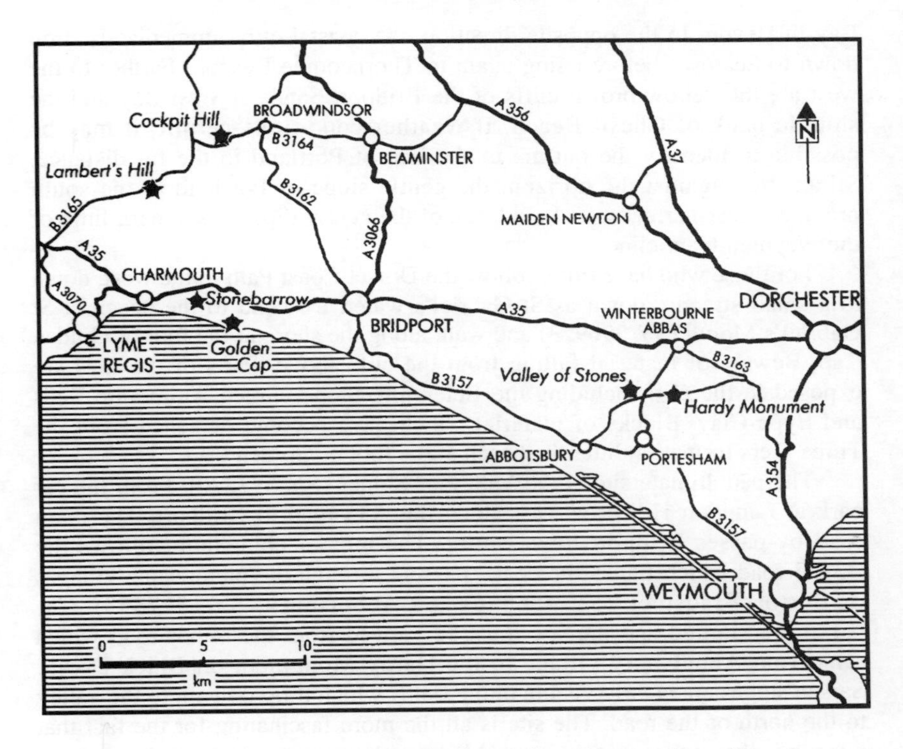

Figure 7. Suggested route for studying the denudational history of west Dorset

From Lambert's Hill, the suggested route moves to the coast at Golden Cap (SY 407923), the highest sea cliff in southern England. Drive south-west along the B3165 road until the main east-west A35 trunk-road is reached. Turn east, by-passing the village of Charmouth and passing through Morcombelake. A small car park is located to the south of the Morcombelake to Chideock road, on the north side of Langdon Hill (SY 413932). Access is via a track, known locally as Muddy Ford Lane, which leaves the A35 main road (at SY 412935) just before the latter starts to descend towards Chideock village. A footpath links the car park and the summit of Golden Cap. The footpath, which is signposted by the National Trust, initially runs through woodland along the east side of Langdon Hill before crossing a field and rising to the top of the sea cliff.

On a clear day spectacular views stretch in all directions. To the north, the flat-topped hills and accordant summits can be seen stretching far inland beyond the Vale of Marshwood. The eye can follow the coast to the west past the landslide complexes of Stonebarrow Hill and Black Ven to the town of Lyme Regis and, beyond that, the landslips of Downlands Cliff and Pinhay

Bay in Devon. In the opposite direction, the coastal cliffs immediately drop down to Seatown before rising again to Thorncombe Beacon. Farther to the west are the yellow-brown cliffs of the Bridport Sands at West Bay and the shingle bank of Chesil Beach. If weather conditions permit, it may be possible to identify the outline of the Isle of Portland in the far distance. Silhouetted against the horizon, the gentle slope of Portland to the south provides near-perfect visual evidence of the gently dipping southern limb of the Weymouth anticline.

For those who have time, follow the Dorset Coast Path to the west, down to a small stream known as St Gabriel's water. Descend to the beach at St Gabriel's Mouth (SY 396923) and walk along the shore at the foot of Golden Cap. Beware of material falling from the cliff above. Parts of the Lias are exposed in the cliff including the Belemnite Stone, Green Ammonite Beds and Eype Clay. Blocks of material which have become detached from the Three Tiers formation litter the beach at the foot of Golden Cap.

The penultimate site is the Valley of Stones (SY 597876). From the car park at Langdon Hill drive east along the A35 road to Bridport. The main road by-passes Bridport town centre. The most scenic route follows the B3157 road which flanks the coast, passing through the picturesque villages of Burton Bradstock (SY 486896) and Abbotsbury (SY 577853). Car parking is limited and the site must be viewed from the minor road which runs from Abbotsbury village to the Hardy Monument on Black Down. Sarsen stones are clearly visible in the fields which drop down into the valley to the north of the road. The site is all the more fascinating for the fact that none of the stones are *in situ*. All have been moved either by natural agencies, such as Pleistocene solifluction, or by man.

Finally, drive to the top of Black Down (SY 613876), some 20km east-south-east of Golden Cap. The Hardy Monument on the summit forms a prominent landmark around which there are many exposures of the Bagshot Gravels. A car park is available. Once again, superb views spread all around back towards the Vale of Marshwood in the west, to Dorchester and the valley of the Frome river in the north-east and away to Weymouth and the Isle of Portland in the south-east. The accordance in summits is again visible and, despite the uncertainty of reconstructions of former land surfaces, this final site is perhaps the best location from which to assimilate the evidence available so far and identify within the landscape key pointers to the denudational history of this part of the country.

LANDSLIDE TYPES AND PROCESSES

Robert J. Allison

Introduction

The term mass movement applies to processes which transport soil and rock from high to low ground, due to gravitational displacement. The processes manifest themselves in different forms of landslide and, as Hutchinson (1968) and Bromhead (1986) note, the variety of slope movements is so great that a rigorous classification is hardly possible. Not only do slope movements vary in form, origin and magnitude but they also include everything from shallow failures which are usually associated with weathered material, to deep-seated displacements of large rock masses.

It is not the aim here to provide a comprehensive summary of all types of slope instability since reviews of this nature abound (Skempton and Hutchinson, 1969; Varnes, 1978; Hansen, 1984; Bromhead, 1986, for example). Instead, the types of mass movement present along the Dorset coast will be described. Particular attention will be paid to mudslides, the most important landslide type at Black Ven (SY 355929), Higher Sea Lane (SY 363930), Golden Cap (SY 407923), Stonebarrow Hill (SY 375927).

The mass movements mantling the coastal slopes in west Dorset are best considered in four groups: slides, flows, falls and topples. In slides the base of the landslide mass remains in contact with underlying rock and a shear or slip surface develops between the two. Movement is progressive, propagating out from one point. If sliding material becomes highly disaggregated and very wet, it can be classified as a flow. Falls, on the other hand, usually take place from *in situ* engineering soil or rock and result in the complete and almost immediate detachment of material. Falls are rapid events which vary considerably in size. Topples can be considered to be a type of fall but they can be classified separately, due to the precise nature of movement and the constraints governing failure.

Some types of landslide are characteristic of *in situ* materials which have not previously been displaced. Others comprise debris from an earlier mass movement, which is frequently weathered and subsequently moving by a second mechanism. An example is where blocks of rock fall from steep cliffs on to a mudslide, become integrated within the moving mass and change to a flow when the moving debris becomes highly saturated with water. This emphasises the fact that while specific mass movement mechanisms may be identified, landslides will often change from one form to another as they progress from high points to low points through space.

Slides

Slides comprise material which has been displaced across a clearly definable surface or surfaces, separating *in situ* rock from the moving mass. Numerous classifications have been proposed based on factors like movement rate, the characteristics of the unstable material and the shape of the slip surface. Movement or strain is progressive as the landslide material becomes increasingly displaced from its original location. Three types of slide movement are common along the west Dorset coast: translational slides, rotational slides and mudslides.

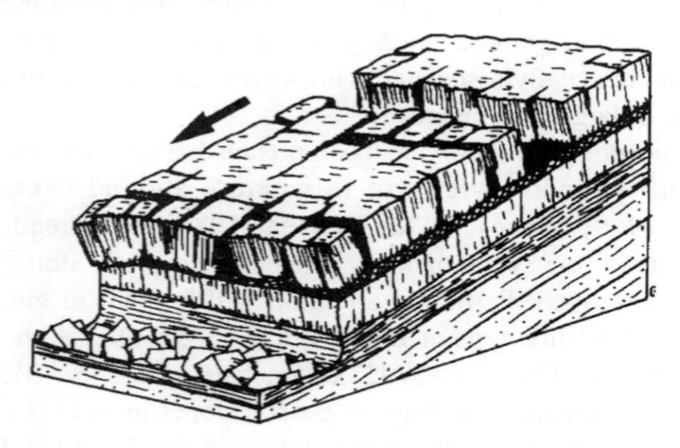

Figure 8. Characteristics of translational slides.

Translational slides move across more or less planar surfaces (Figure 8). The moving mass may slip across the original ground surface particularly on low angle slopes, on intersecting discontinuities which outcrop in a cliff face in such a way that they promote instability, or at the base of a weathered boundary layer. Movement occurs across a slip surface. Slip surfaces are characteristically shallow and often located within 1m to 2m of the surface of the ground. The upper surface of a translational slide generally does not tilt during displacement and recently slipped blocks retain their original shape.

Translational slides may develop in both lithified rocks, such as limestones and sandstones, and more clayey materials. In the former instance, joints within the rock mass will result in separate blocks of material which are prone to sliding on discontinuity surfaces such as bedding planes. Shearing may occasionally take place through the solid rock as well as across pre-existing fractures within the rock. In poorly lithified sediments, translational slides are usually associated with weathering. Where a translational slide is joint bounded at its sides the landslide can move across low angle surfaces.

In theory, translational slide movements can be infinite, particularly if the slip surface is inclined at an angle greater than the friction angle of the slope and the shear resistance across the slip surface is low. In practice, translational slides usually rapidly fragment during movement, becoming incorporated in other types of landslide. Displacements involve linear motion and occasionally, if the slipped block is particularly large, a fault-bounded chasm or graben forms. An excellent example is found at Bindon (Pitts, 1981 1983) southwest of Lyme Regis. At Bindon a large back-scar in Chalk and Upper Greensand is fronted by a graben structure 750m long (SY 293898).

Rotational slides have internal, concave-upward, deep-seated slip surfaces (Figure 9). They are often found in actively eroding cliffs and are one of the major types of slope movement along the west Dorset coast. Sliding is rotational about an axis parallel to the slope crest and frequently the precise shape of the slip surface is influenced by faults, joints and bedding.

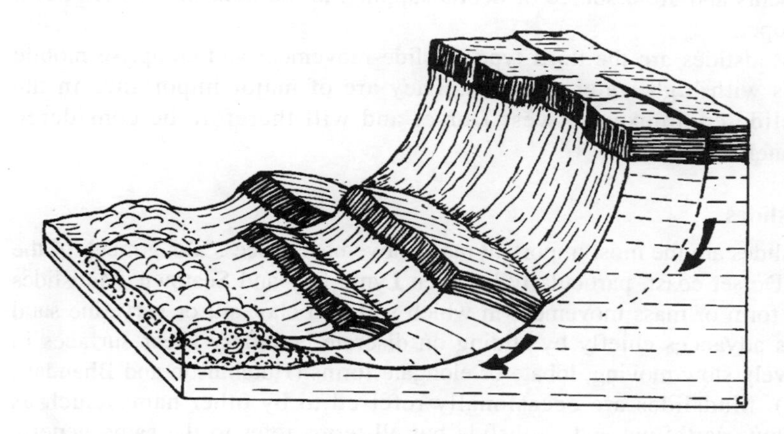

Figure 9. Characteristics of rotational slides.

Once movement has commenced, slippage along the line of the original ground surface will appear to be downward with little apparent rotation, although there may be evidence of back tilting. The tilt will cause a hollow to develop between the upper surface of the slipped mass and the newly exposed back scar at the head of the slope. Sediment which is weathered and eroded from the back scar becomes trapped behind the tilted block and ponds of water frequently develop at the contact between the landslide and in situ rock. The ponds are often seasonal, drying up during warmer periods or when precipitation is low and acting as a source of lubrication to the slip surface at other times. Damage to property from rotational slides can be severe. At the top of Stonebarrow Hill, for example, a building was displaced from its original position on the hill summit by rotational movements in 1942 and is now gradually descending towards the sea.

Initially, as a rotational slump becomes detached from the head of a slope, it supports the stable ground behind it. As movement continues, the ground at the head of the slope will be increasingly unsupported and the potential for a new failure increases (Richards and Lorriman, 1987). As a consequence, rotational slips frequently develop in sequence and multiple failures appear stacked one behind the other. In such a situation the constituent failures may combine to form a common basal shear surface. Excellent examples of multiple rotational failures occur at Stonebarrow Hill and Black Ven. At Stonebarrow multiple rotational slides mantle a large section of the Fairy Dell landslide complex. At Black Ven rotational slides are abundant towards the rear of the unstable ground in the Cretaceous sediments and are a source of debris supplied to the mudslides lower down the slope.

Mudslides are the third type of slide movement and comprise mobile debris with high water contents. They are of major importance in the landslide complexes of west Dorset and will therefore be considered separately.

Mudslides

Mudslides are the most important mass movement process along much of the west Dorset coast, particularly between Lyme Bay and Seatown. Mudslides are a form of mass movement in which softened clay, silt or very fine sand debris advances chiefly by sliding on discrete boundary shear surfaces in relatively slow moving, lobate or elongate forms (Hutchinson and Bhandari, 1971). Mudslides are occasionally referred to by other names such as mudflow, earthflow and earthslide but all terms refer to the same generic feature (Figure 10).

Mudslides have three morphological zones. At the head of the slope a bowl or headward feeder forms the main area of supply. The headward feeder is backed by a steep rear scar or small cliff developed in the in situ material and marks the junction between stable and unstable ground. Supply from the rear scar is by a combination of topples, falls and the gradual processes of weathering and erosion. Occasionally rear scars form on the leading edge of other types of movement, such as rotational failures. Adjacent source areas may form a regular series of embayments (Hutchinson, 1983). Soil moisture and pore water pressure distributions are very irregular in the headward feeder. During unstable conditions debris is shunted out of the bowl to lower parts of the system.

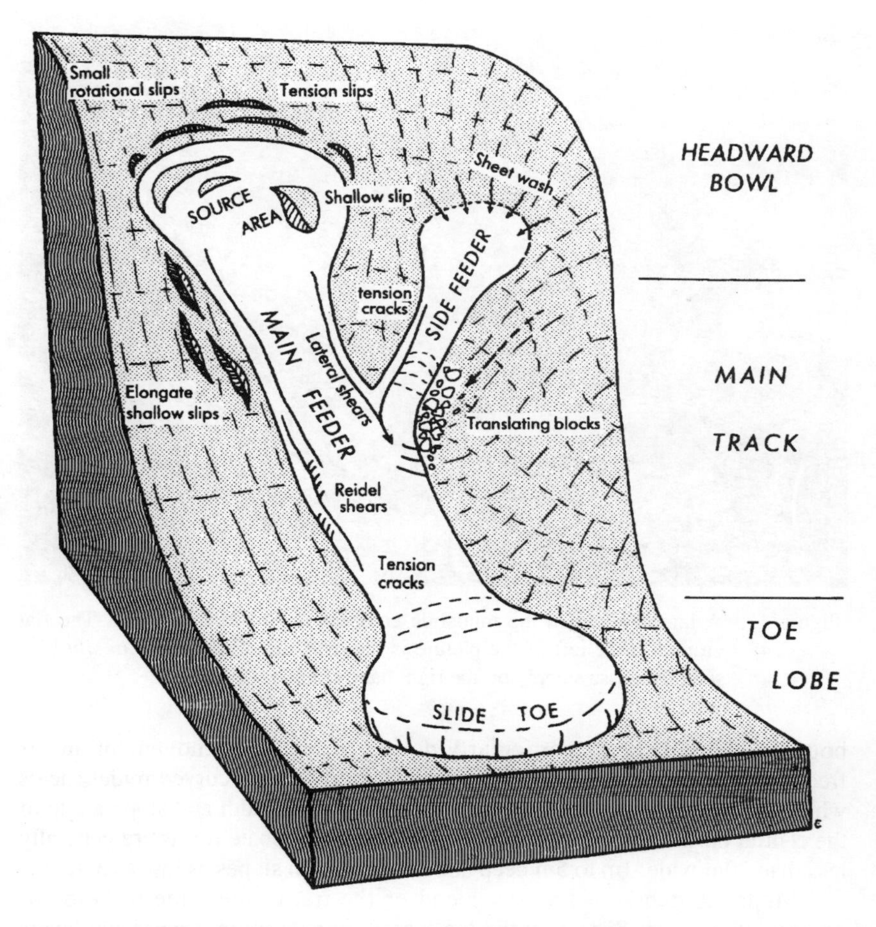

Figure 10. Characteristics of mudslides *(after Brunsden, 1973)*.

The track, which forms the central part of a mudslide, is usually steep, straight, and forms a zone of transport for material passing from the crest to the toe of the slope. The base of the track is marked by a slip surface which is parallel to the ground surface. As mudslide debris moves out of the accumulation zone and into the track it becomes increasingly broken up and softened. Short tracks produce lobate mudslides, a common feature along coastal cliffs. Long tracks result in more sinuous forms which are less common in coastal areas. Examples of lobate mudslides are found at numerous points along the west Dorset coast. The track is sharply defined by

Figure 11. A lateral shear in the mudslide complex at Stonebarrow Hill. The flat ground to the left of the picture is the mudslide track, while *in situ* Lias sediments rise steeply on the right hand side.

bounding lateral shears particularly during or just after movement and is frequently covered by pressure ridges, tension cracks and curved reidel shears which develop at the edges of the moving mass. The width and slope angle of the central portion of a mudslide vary considerably. Lobate forms are generally less than 20m wide, 1m to 5m deep and may occur on slopes as low as 3° to 4°.

Mudslide debris at the lower end of the track enters the toe lobe or accumulation zone. Supply to the toe lobe is frequently by successive layers of material. Two components can be identified in the accumulation zone; an upper, flatter area, with slope angles between 1° and 5° and a convex down slope end with slope angles between 15° and 25° The accumulation zone has a sharp basal shear surface, internal longitudinal shears where the centre of the mass thrusts forward and internal shear surfaces or thrust planes (Brunsden, 1984). The toe lobe of a coastal mudslide can be truncated by the sea and the leading edge is often surrounded by one or more boulder arcs which mark previous maximum limits of the mudslide. Accumulation zones frequently act as a support to debris in the track. If under these circumstances the toe lobe is washed away by the sea, material higher up the slope will be unloaded and movement rates increase.

Figure 12. Tension cracks opening up towards the rear of the Black Ven mudslides.

Identifying the morphological zones of a mudslide is an important prerequisite to instrumentation and monitoring. Both the initiation of movement and mudslide re-activation are due to the effects of key variables including the water budget, pore water pressure, soil moisture and material supply. The individual variables can be linked to form a process-response system (Brunsden, 1973), where the effects of each parameter on instability and movement are taken into account (Figure 13).

Much work has been undertaken recently to elucidate patterns of mudslide movement. In general terms, mudslide movement frequently approximates to the form described by rheologists as plug flow (Johnson, 1970). True plug flow involves an edge or bottom layer of variable thickness, which deforms by internal changes and which encloses a central plug acting as a rigid 'sliding' body. In other instances, movement can be considered to be parabolic and associated with flow caused by continuous internal deformation. In very wet conditions debris will truly flow by internal deformation. Simple plug or parabolic sliding may be complicated by internal shears, multiple lateral shears and a complex basal slip surface. The overall result in these circumstances is a complex situation where the central part of a mudslide moves out from the lateral material and different parts of the mudslide move at different velocities.

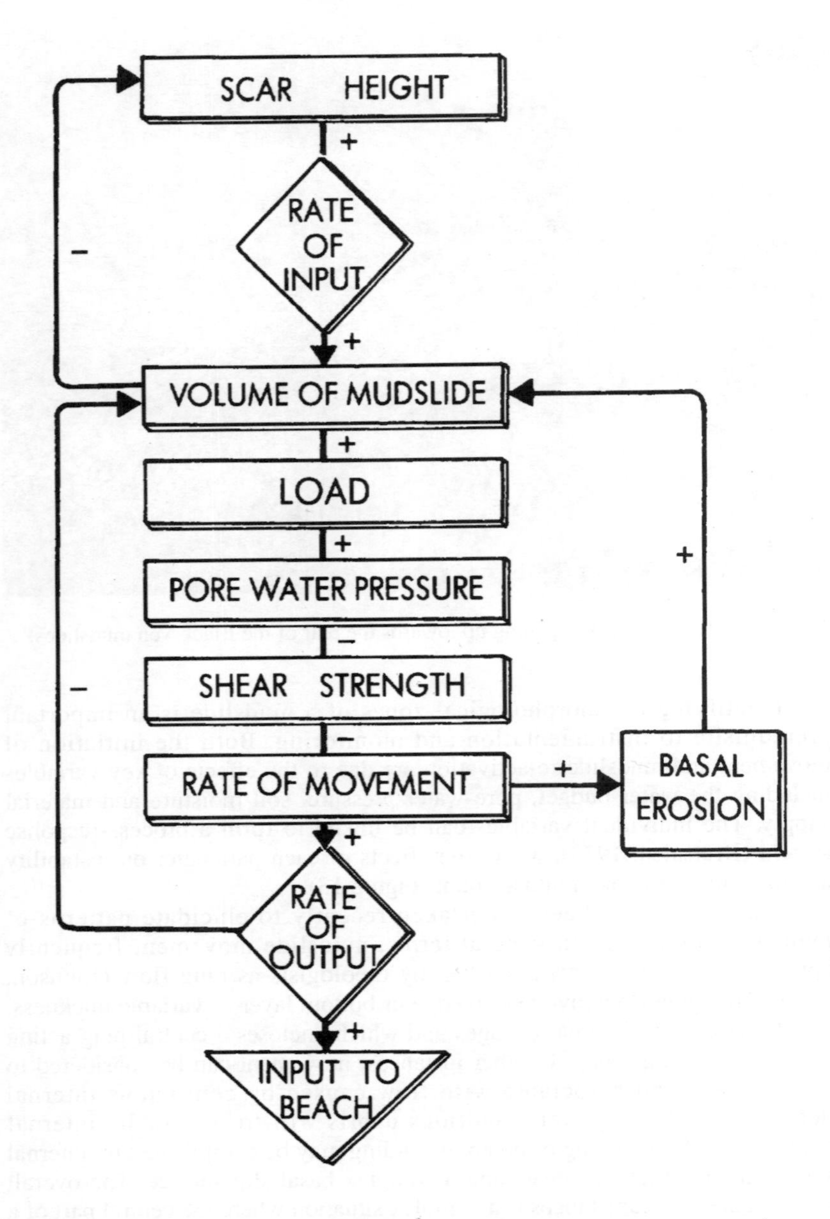

Figure 13. Flow diagram illustrating the process-response characterisitics of mudslides *(after Brunsden, 1973)*.

Flows

Flows are rapid mass movements characteristic of extremely wet conditions, when unconsolidated materials become supercharged with water and reach moisture contents far above their liquid limit (Figure 14). Flowing debris is often recognised as a viscous fluid and can be subdivided as either debris flows, sandflows or mudflows, depending on the matrix particle size characteristics. Debris flows, for example, have a high percentage of coarse fragments, whereas mudflows consist of material containing at least and usually more than 50% sand, silt and clay size particles.

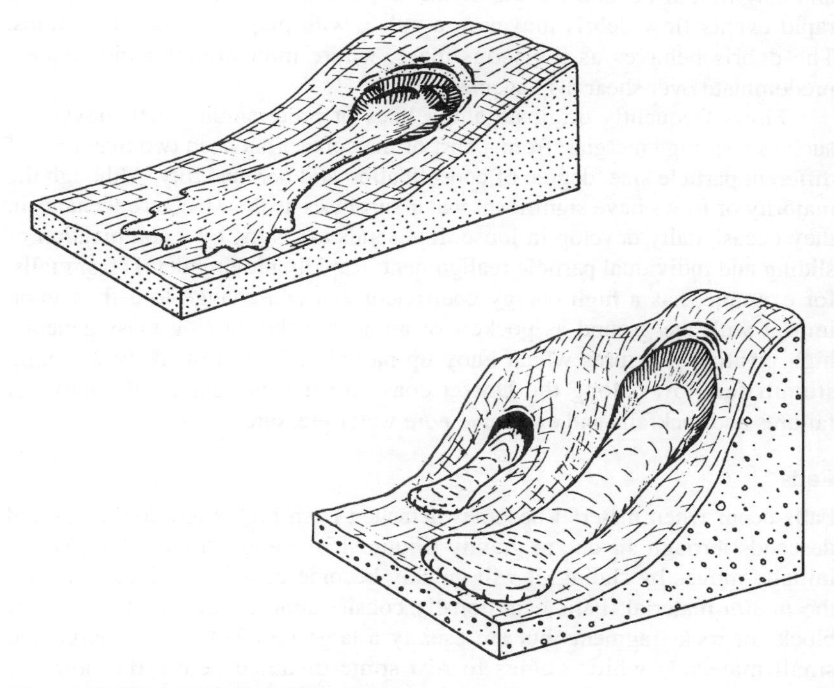

Figure 14. Characteristics of flows.

The mobilising effect of water is an important part of the flow process and consequently the moving mass lacks any internal structure. Also a material strength parameter, known as the brittleness index (IB), is important. The brittleness index is a mechanical property, based on peak and residual strengths. A soft sediment which displays only a small difference between peak strength and residual strength values is more likely to develop flowslide movements under high pore water pressures than is a rock material where the peak strength is considerably greater than the associated residual value. Flow displacements are large, frequently shunting highly mobile debris over the top of other types of landslide and making identification of the slip surface difficult. The speed of flow movements is highly dependent on material cohesion, the angle of slope over which movement takes place and the degree of material saturation. Mudflows, for example, are often categorised by movement velocities between 10m min^{-1} and 1000m min^{-1} and the ability to move over slopes of less than one degree. Sediment moving in flows occasionally liquifies, tumbling down slope along gullies, in stream channels and surging out beyond the toe of the slope at high velocities. During such rapid events flow debris moves in a pulse, with major internal distortions. The debris behaves as a viscous mass, where inter-granular movements predominate over shear displacements.

Flows frequently originate along lines of preferential water movement such as a spring emerging from a cliff or the contact between two materials of different particle size, degree of consolidation and permeability. Although the majority of flows have significant water surpluses as their trigger mechanism, they occasionally develop in loose, fine sands and silts, by a combination of sliding and individual particle realignment. Rapidly moving debris from falls, for example, has a high energy coefficient and can change to a flow upon impact with the ground as pockets of air within the moving mass generate high positive pressures which buoy up particles. The most likely initiating stimuli for flows along the Dorset coast are the movement of rotational failures and rockfalls and excessive pore water pressures.

Falls

Falls occur when material becomes detached from high angle free faces and descends through air due to gravity (Figure 15). Although the falling debris initially moves by sliding, it will quickly become completely detached from the *in situ* material. Falls occasionally consist almost entirely of individual blocks or rock fragments but are usually a large jumbled mass of large and small materials which comes to rest some distance below the point of detachment. As a group or type of mass movement, rockfalls are difficult to characterise. It is possible to argue that natural rock falls are evident on any cliff face, for example, and that when any mass of rock becomes detached from its surrounding material a fall has occurred.

Blocks of rock involved in falls become detached along lines of structural weakness such as bedding planes and joints in the *in situ* material. The blocks fragment, occasionally during motion, but usually upon impact with the ground. The immediate cause of detachment will be a change in the stress distribution within the rock mass, which is frequently a consequence of

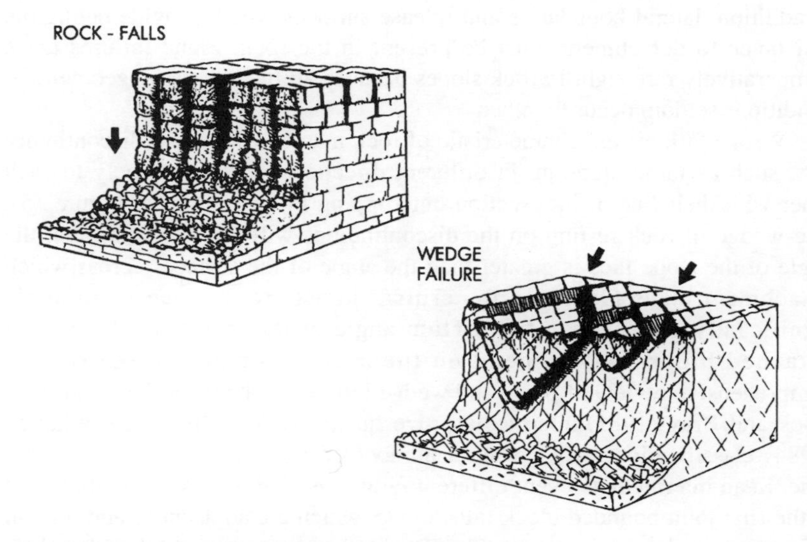

Figure 15. Examples of fall mechanisms in rock masses.

weathering and changes in pore water pressure within the fissures. The resulting debris often forms a scree stacked against the base of the cliff but alternatively may supply other types of landslide, such as mudslides and flows, which then transport the debris further down slope.

Falls vary in size. Whalley (1984), for example, outlined a classification based on the volume of material. Debris falls are movements of less than $10m^3$, boulder falls describe displacements of $10m^3$ to $100m^3$ and blockfalls are mass movements of more than $100m^3$. It should be noted however, that classification by volume is generally poor because no consideration is given to process. In short, it is frequently difficult to sub-divide rockfalls into different categories.

Along the west Dorset coast small debris falls (as defined by Whalley, 1984), which involve the removal of individual and superficial blocks from cliff faces, are frequent. Failure surfaces are invariably joint controlled and the orientation of discontinuities determines the specific type of block detachment. In some cases failure is a response to gravity stresses while in others it is due to the undermining of the base of the slope by mudslides, seepage and weathering. Two types of debris fall can be identified.

Plane failures develop when the primary surface across which detachment occurs strikes parallel to the slope (+/- 20°), outcrops in the cliff face and dips at an angle greater than the angle of friction across the surface.

In addition, lateral boundaries and release surfaces which provide negligible resistance to detachment must be present in the rock. Plane failures are a comparatively rare sight in rock slopes because all the necessary geometrical conditions seldom occur together.

Wedge failures are characteristic of rock masses where two discontinuity sets, such as joints trending in different directions, strike obliquely to each other with their line of intersection outcropping in the cliff face (Figure 15). The wedge of rock resting on the discontinuities will fail providing that the angle of the slope face is greater than the angle of the surfaces across which detachment takes place and the critical joints are inclined at an angle significantly greater than the friction angle of the material. The size of detached blocks will depend on the spacing of discontinuities. A comprehensive review of plane and wedge failure mechanisms is provided by Hoek and Bray (1981).Intermediate size falls, boulder falls by the Whalley (1984) classification, occur when a number of rock blocks fail at the same time. In an intermediate event different failure mechanisms may combine and as the first joint bounded block falls, others which are adjacent to and rely on it for support also become unstable. Blockfalls are common in the Lias cliffs between Charmouth (SY 366929) and West Bay (SY 462904).

Rockfall debris almost always comes to rest at the foot of the cliff from which it has become detached. The resulting talus deposits vary in size and morphology. If rockfall activity occurs along the entire length of a cliff line, an apron of fallen rock blocks will be found at the base of the slope (Figure 16). The accumulated debris gradually breaks down due to weathering and, depending on the precise location of the deposit, will either become incorporated in other types of mass movement or be removed by processes such as marine erosion. At Black Ven (SY 355929), for example, talus from the Lias cliff weathers down and becomes incorporated within the mudslides which cover the Black Ven marl benches. At the foot of Stonebarrow Hill (SY 375927) and Golden Cap (SY 407923) on the other hand, the Lias cliff backs the beach and any rockfall debris is subject to direct erosion by the sea.

At localised points along a cliff where rockfall activity has been particularly active, debris cones may develop (Figure 14). Debris cones can be identified in the field as small conical buttresses of material which often have an identifiable failure scar above them, highlighting the area on the cliff from which the fallen material has become detached. Occasionally debris cones become superimposed on talus slopes, representing a situation where localised rockfalls of high magnitude have occurred along cliffs which are cumulatively susceptible to lower frequency activity. Examples can again be found in the Lias at Black Ven and Stonebarrow Hill.

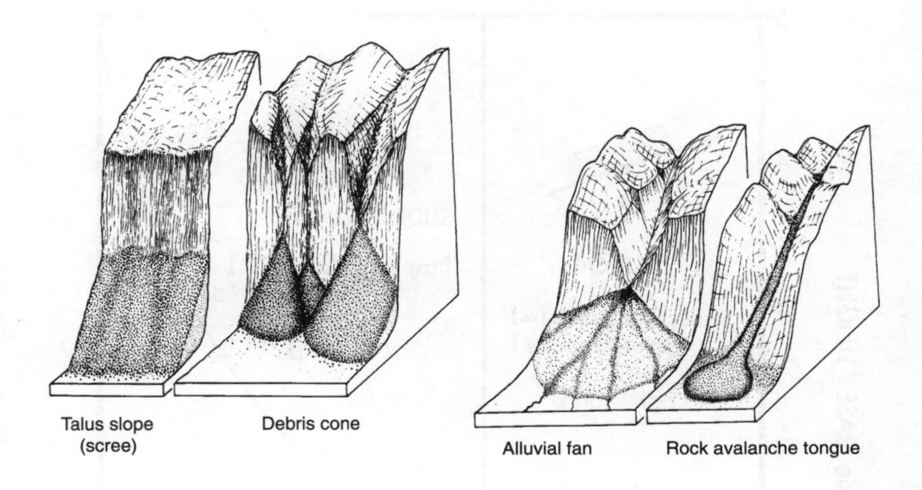

Figure 16. Types of talus deposit *(after Selby, 1982)*

When larger rockfalls occur, the resulting debris may run out and away from the base of the cliff, rather than collecting as a talus slope or debris cone. This tends to be the case when the detached material comprises large blocks of rock. Hutchinson (1971) discusses the run-out phenomenon in the Chalk cliffs of Kent. Similar processes and deposits can be identified in west Dorset along the Chalk cliffs at St Oswald's Bay (SY 811803). Deposits of this type are sometimes referred to as rock avalanches (Selby, 1981) but such a term implies massive volumes of moving material.

Topples

Toppling failures are controlled by relationships between the dimensions of joint bounded blocks in the slope, the friction angle of the rock, the angle of the rock face and the orientation of the cliff relative to the discontinuity pattern (Figure 17). Although topples are technically a type of rockfall, they form a distinct group. During movement the dislodged blocks of rock have forward rotation about a pivot point below or low down in the rock block under the action of gravity and forces exerted by adjacent blocks. Topples frequently displace large amounts of material but they are found in a limited number of locations because specific lithological and structural controls are necessary for the toppling mechanism to be effective.

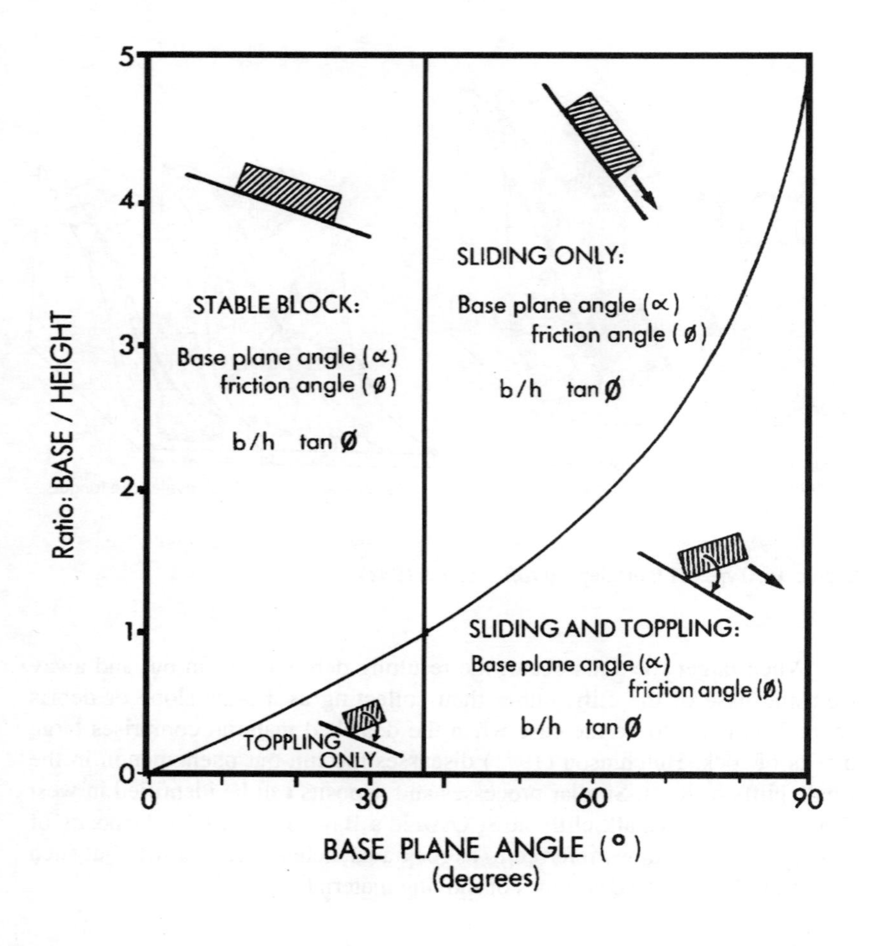

Figure 17. Limiting conditions for toppling failures *(after Hoek & Bray, 1981)*

There are different types of topple (Figure 18). Flexural toppling is characteristic of continuous columns of rock which are separated by well developed, steeply dipping discontinuities. The rock blocks bend forward and break away in flexure. Block toppling occurs when individual columns of rock are separated by widely spaced joints and material at the toe of the slope is pushed forward by the loading effect of overturning columns behind.
Some sliding may take place at the toe, allowing further topples to develop higher up the slope. Block topples often have the appearance of a stairway.

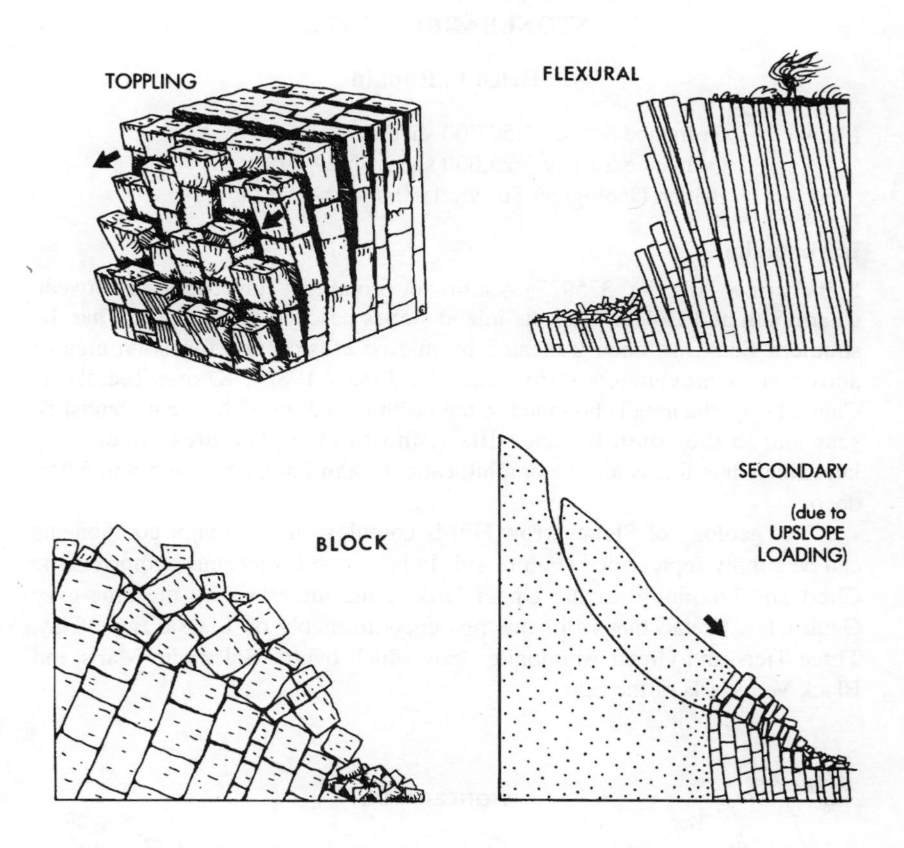

Figure 18. Types of toppling failure *(after Hoek & Bray, 1981)*.

Topples are common on the steep cliffs below Stonebarrow. Occasionally weaker layers of rock at the base of the cliff fail and the column sags downward and backwards.

With block flexure toppling, pseudo-continuous flexure occurs along columns divided by numerous cross joints. Consequently block flexure is characterised by many small movements on the cross joints which cumulatively give rise to a significant total displacement. There are a number of secondary toppling mechanisms such as those triggered by undercutting at the toe of the slope, either by natural processes such as marine erosion or due to the influence of man. The most detailed descriptions of topples have been given by De Freitas and Watters (1973) and Hoek and Bray (1981).

STONEBARROW HILL

Helen L. Rudkin

Maps: Ordnance Survey 1:50,000 sheet 193.
Ordnance Survey 1:25,000 sheet SY29/39.
British Geological Survey 1:50,000 sheet 326.

Introduction

Stonebarrow Hill (SY 375927) is a broad, prominent ridge, located between Charmouth and Golden Cap. Its inland slopes descend to the River Char. Its southern flank has been truncated by marine erosion and forms an area of active mass movements (Brunsden and Jones, 1980). Known locally as Cain's Folly, the area is bounded to the north by a 30m high arcuate landslide scar and to the south by sea-cliffs rising to 60m. The area covered by landslides thus forms a large amphitheatre 1400m long, 85m high and 350m deep.

The geology of Stonebarrow Hill is complex but the major components can be simply represented (Figure 19). In brief, the Cretaceous comprises the Chert and Foxmould of the Upper Greensand, underlain by the blue-grey Gault Clay. Cretaceous sediments rest unconformably on Liassic Eype Clay, Three Tiers and Green Ammonite Beds which overly Belemnite Marls and Black Ven Marls of the Lias.

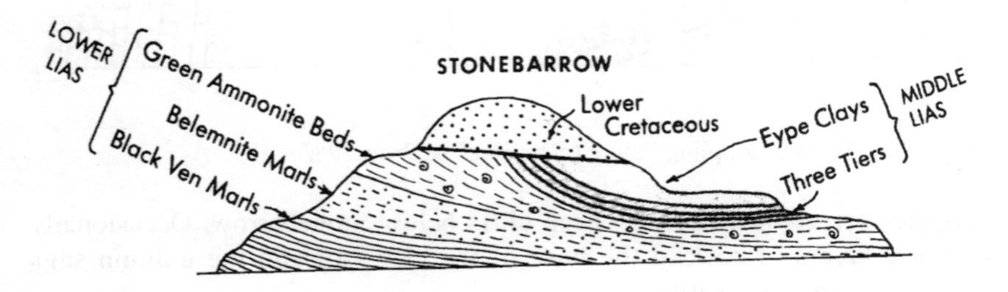

Figure 19. Major geological components of Stonebarrow Hill *(after House, 1989).*

The inland slopes

The inland slopes of Stonebarrow Hill, especially on the eastern valley side of the River Char, are mantled with degraded landslides (Brunsden and Jones, 1972). The unstable slopes are due to a permeable layer of Gault and Upper Greensand lying on top of heavily overconsolidated clays (Figure 20). The steep angle Upper Greensand slopes are primarily a degradation zone, while the Gault and Lias are covered by thick spreads of mass movement debris and head, forming lower angle slope sections. Geomorphological mapping by Brunsden and Jones (1972) has revealed the following landslide forms using Hutchinson's (1967, 1968) classification: rotational slides, successive rotational slides, irregular successive slips, successive undulations, translational slides and mudflows.

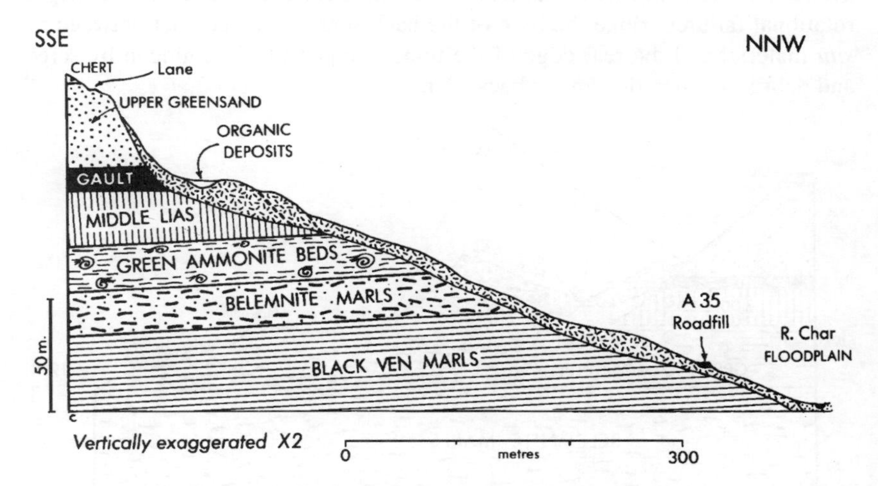

Figure 20. Cross-section of Stonebarrow Hill landward slopes *(after Brunsden & Jones, 1976).*

There are recent signs of new landslide activity on lower parts of the landward slopes of Stonebarrow, although it is difficult to identify either individual features or their overall distribution due to the masking effects of vegetation and agriculture. Re- activation of the ancient slips is thought to be due to two causes. First, a number of slumps have occurred along the banks of the River Char due to fluvial incision at the base of the slope. Second, the initial construction of and engineering work during the 1970's along the line of the A35 Charmouth to Morcombelake trunk road has promoted slip due to a combination of weight, vibration, toe slope disruption and impeded drainage.

The coastal slopes

The most spectacular landslides at Stonebarrow Hill are on the seaward facing slopes. At sea level 40m to 50m high cliffs are overlooked by a large mass movement amphitheatre approximately 1400m long, 350m deep and

85m high, known as Fairy Dell (Arber, 1941; Brunsden and Jones, 1976). There are clear lithological controls on the slope failures. Cretaceous Chert, Upper Greensand and Gault overly strata of the Middle and Lower Lias (Figure 21). Debris covered benches have evolved at the junction of the Gault and the Green Ammonite Beds. A steep cliff marking the boundary of the stable ground has developed in the Chert and Foxmould. The rear cliff is gradually breaking away as new rotational failures develop. Multiple rotational failures fringe the base of the back scar but the contact between *in situ* material and the rear edge of the upper slipped block is hidden by scree and debris weathered from the back scar.

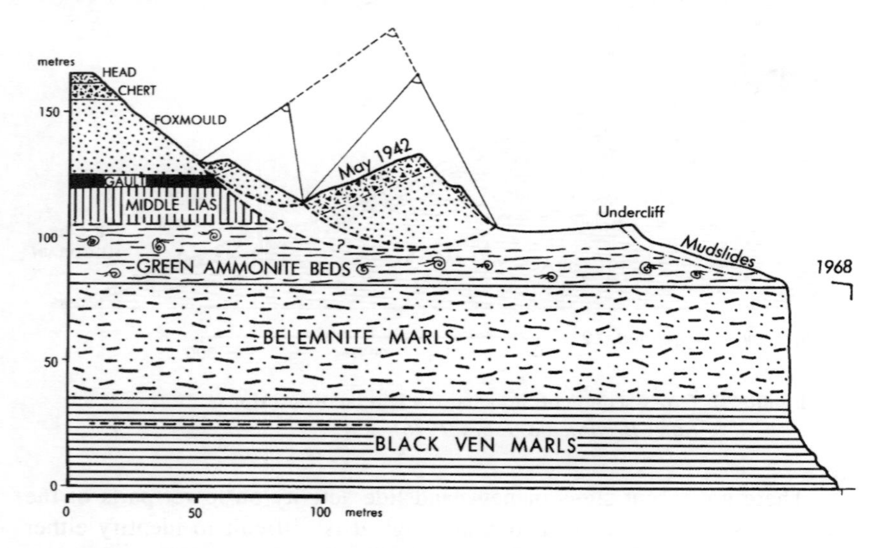

Figure 21. Stonebarrow Hill cross-section based on 1989 air photographs.

Across the upper slopes of Stonebarrow Hill three rotational failures, which move sporadically towards the sea, lie stacked one behind the other (Figure 22). The lower of the three rotational slides is highly degraded and the tilt of the Upper Greensand strata contained within it indicates a high degree of circular displacement. This rotational slide occurred before the first Ordnance Survey of 1887. The second slump in the sequence can be dated to 14th May 1942 (Lang, 1942, 1944), when a cliff section 20m wide subsided, displacing a ground surface area of approximately 7500m^2. Evidence exists of further rotational slides behind the 1942 feature. The latest slumps are the smallest. Movement of the rotational slides towards the sea removes lateral support from the rear scar, eventually leading to the detachment of another block.

Figure 22. The Cretaceous back scar and rotational slides at Stonebarrow Hill.

Recession of the back scar is not just by rotational failure. Measured weathering and erosion rates using erosion pins estimated a net loss of 0.15 metres per annum during the 1960's (Brunsden, 1974). Nevertheless, the evolution of the landslide complex at the head of the slope is primarily governed by high magnitude and low frequency events.

Mudslides and mudflows 1m to 2m deep feed down slope from the leading edge of the pre-1887 rotational failure, moving across an undercliff developed in the Middle Lias and over the cliff edge which drops to sea level. (Figure 23). The mudslides either erode into the rotational landslides or form steep, circular hollows in the undercliff (Brunsden, 1973). The lower cliff has formed in the Belemnite and Black Ven Marls. During periods of significant landslide activity mudslide movement can exceed 90 metres per annum. Movement is seasonal, increasing in the winter months when large amounts of debris are pushed over the cliff edge.

The geology of Stonebarrow thus allows the identification of three 'morphodynamic zones' (Brunsden and Jones, 1976). Zone A comprises the upper area, developed on Cretaceous deposits. A back scar has developed in the Upper Greensand and Chert. The scar has a maximum height of 45m, slope angles of 50° to 70° and is partially covered at its base by scree material

Figure 23. The Lias cliff at Stonebarrow Hill. The talus deposits at the foot of the slope represent landslide debris which has been shunted over the cliff edge.

resting at a mean angle of 35°. Zone A includes rotational landslides which have become detached from the crest of Stonebarrow Hill. Between detachment the blocks are subject to weathering and small scale erosion processes (Brunsden and Jones, 1980).

Zone B comprises the lower area of landslides. It forms an undercliff in the Middle Lias and comprises small rotational slides, debris accumulation areas, mudslides, mudflows and slumps. Zone B effectively forms a zone of transport for landslide debris being shunted from Zone A to Zone C. Liassic and Cretaceous sediments become intermixed in Zone B as they feed down-slope.

Zone C consists of near vertical, 40m to 60m high sea cliffs. They fail by topples, sags and falls. Mudslide debris shunts over the crest of the slope, occasionally pulling away sections of the cliff top due to friction effects and the weight of the sliding overburden. Debris collects at the foot of the cliff, reflecting the combination of mudslide and cliff collapse mechanisms. The overall result is a complex sequence of interactions which were drawn together by Brunsden and Jones (1980) in the following evolutionary model for the Stonebarrow Hill landslides, based on a series of maps and vertical air photographs between 1887 and 1969 and ground survey data.

Marine erosion of the sea cliffs removes the basal debris and leads to continuing cliff retreat. This has the direct effect of increasing the rate of debris transport causing the undermining of the undercliff. Through time large, intact blocks of material weather and disintegrate to smaller units. The result is increased slope convexity leading to large scale failure of the undercliff. Consequently the mudslide basins become inundated by degraded landslide blocks. Mudslide debris feeds over the edge of the sea cliff (Zone C). and as the landslides move seaward support to the base of the rear cliff is removed, resulting in the retreat of the cliff through further failure. It has been proposed by Brunsden and Jones (1976) that marine erosion of the sea cliff sets up a 'zone of aggression' moving inland. Debris is thus gradually redistributed in a down-slope direction across the whole of the cliff and the cycle is completed when failure of the rear cliff sends a pulse of material towards the sea as a large block becomes detached and moves away from the crest of the slope.

When supply of material to the toe of the slope exceeds removal, sea cliff retreat slows down. If, on the other hand, debris supply to the base of the sea cliff is reduced, removal may well exceed supply. In these circumstances, the retreat rate of the lower cliff (Zone C) will reach a maximum, stimulating increased activity back up the slope. Complex responses, feed-back mechanisms and energy transfers thus take place through the landslides in a cyclic manner.

The history of landslide activity at the site spans over 100 years but is dominated by two major events. Prior to the Ordnance Survey of 1887 a large section of the rear cliff failed by rotational sliding. It is believed that the cliff retreated by up to 80m, although this figure can only be considered an estimate based on the 1887 Ordnance Survey maps. Remnants of the failure are still present today in the Stonebarrow landslips. The second major failure on 14th May 1942 involved a large section of the central rear scar. The rotating blocks removed two radio location stations and a grove of trees, with the cliff retreating by 28m (Figure 24). Several small failures occurred immediately to the east of the main slide and the effects of the event were felt throughout the whole of the slope (Figure 25).

Figure 24. The rear of the landslide complex at Stonebarrow Hill, showing the displaced and back-tilted radar hut.

Air photograph cover for Stonebarrow now exists for 1969, 1972, 1984 and 1989. By comparing the profile surveyed in 1969 and the results of a recent survey completed in 1989 it is possible to identify a number of changes in morphology. The sea cliff has experienced considerable retreat of approximately 23m. The mass movement complex itself has assumed a much simpler and subdued morphology following the removal of the degraded landslide blocks and failure of the undercliff. Since 1942 no further large

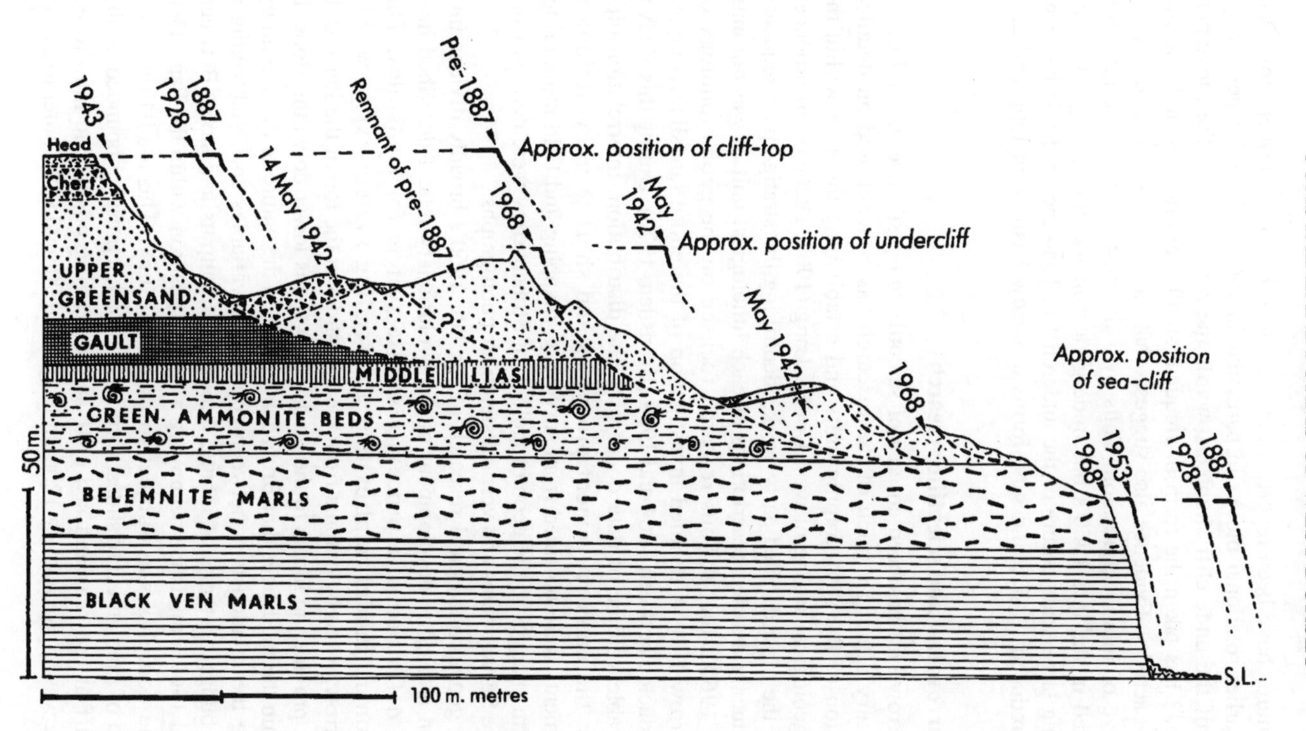

Figure 25. Morphology and slope retreat pattern for Stonebarrow Hill *(after Brunsden & Jones, 1976)*

scale failures have been reported although there has been further movement of the earlier rotational blocks in particular in 1968 and 1984 when a large section of the undercliff shunted towards the sea. Much of the movement since 1942 has taken the form of frequent small scale failures and seasonal mudslide activity. Evidence also suggests that the landslide is experiencing a new wave of inland aggression. Thus over the past 20 years the mudslide monitored in the late 1960's has undergone considerable change in form. Following large scale failure of the undercliff in 1984 the mudslide has been greatly reduced in size and now forms a narrow basin 40m long and 25m wide.

Stonebarrow Hill and scientific research

Stonebarrow Hill has been an area of scientific interest since the end of the last century although much of the research has concentrated on detailed description of the stratigraphic units and establishing the area within the overall geological setting of west Dorset. Lang (1907, 1926, 1936) produced some of the most detailed early work, identifying the stratigraphic sequence and producing detailed descriptions of each lithological unit. It was not until the late 1960's that serious research focused on the geomorphology of Stonebarrow Hill. A detailed investigation of the entire landslide complex was conducted between 1964 and 1969 (Brunsden, 1973). During this study a considerable volume of data concerning the distribution, interrelationships between the mass movement processes and short term evolutionary developments were obtained from surveying, mapping and field monitoring. Long term changes in the geomorphology of Stonebarrow were derived from Ordnance Survey plans and vertical stereo air photographs.

The geomorphological research of the late 1960's broadly divides into two main areas; the development of the evolutionary model described here and the definition of a process-response system for mudslides. The evolutionary model implies that a cascading system exists within Stonebarrow, whereby outputs from the landslides at the top of the Fairy Dell complex provide the inputs to the mudslide systems lower down the slope. It was within the mudslides that Brunsden examined the nature of the system by assessing the relationships between controlling variables and establishing a systems budget in terms of inputs, throughputs, outputs and stores.Between 1964 and 1969 a mudslide occupying a central position within the Fairy Dell landslide complex was subject to detailed study. The mudslide basin consisted of sand and clay slides, forming a broad depression bounded by the undercliff at the rear and sea cliff at the leading edge. The monitored mudslide was approximately 120m in length and 90m wide. In order to assess the rate of input to the mudslide, six lines of erosion pins were installed in the undercliff. Four lines of stakes running across the mudslide track were surveyed every month to determine throughput. Movement, pore water pressure, rainfall, sub-surface movement and stress-strain patterns were also recorded on a monthly basis. Preliminary results revealed a marked seasonal movement pattern with slip reaching maximum values between January and March. Recent advances in the equipment used to monitor the important variables that control slope instability now provide the opportunity to commence new research at Stonebarrow Hill.

Current research at Stonebarrow is aimed at repeating the study completed 20 years ago but equipment installations today are based on recent electronic developments. The study provides a unique opportunity to extend the data record previously collected at this site. The project emphasises the importance of spatial and temporal sampling frameworks in monitoring geomorphological systems.

The primary aims of current research are three-fold. First, to re-evaluate mudslide behaviour with respect to the studies of the late 1960's and assess whether the same mechanisms, controls and rates of movement have been maintained. Second, to establish spatial interrelationships within a mudslide by monitoring the source-to- track and track-to-toe lobe areas. Third, to develop the evolutionary model of the landslide complex at Stonebarrow Hill. It is hoped that the evolutionary model proposed by Brunsden and Jones (1976) can be extended temporally from 1969 to the present day.

Access

Stonebarrow Hill is owned by the National Trust. There are two ways to reach the summit (SY 375927). The first starts in the car park on Charmouth sea front (SY 364931), crossing the bridge over the River Char and following the coastal footpath up the edge of the cliff. The bridge is visible from the car park and the route well signposted. Alternatively, cars can be left at the car park maintained by the National Trust, near the summit of Golden Cap (SY 382933). Access is only suitable for cars and mini-buses and is via a small lane past Newlands. If travelling from Bridport and the east, leave the main A35 road and drive towards Charmouth village. The junction for Stonebarrow turns sharply away to the left (SY 371935) just before the road into the centre of the village swings off to the right. If travelling from Lyme Regis or the west, drive through Charmouth village, keeping to the main street. The road crosses a bridge over the River Char as it leaves the village. As the main road bears away to the left, the small lane to the summit of Stonebarrow Hill is clearly visible, almost on the bend.

Suggested route

The route (Figure 26) commences at the car park at the top of Stonebarrow Hill. Walk back down the lane towards Charmouth village. At points down the lane breaks in the trees provide views over the inland slopes of Stonebarrow Hill. To the untrained eye, degraded landslides can be difficult to identify but the gentle undulations, bumps and hollows in the fields which drop away to the A35 road are all excellent indicators of old landslide activity.

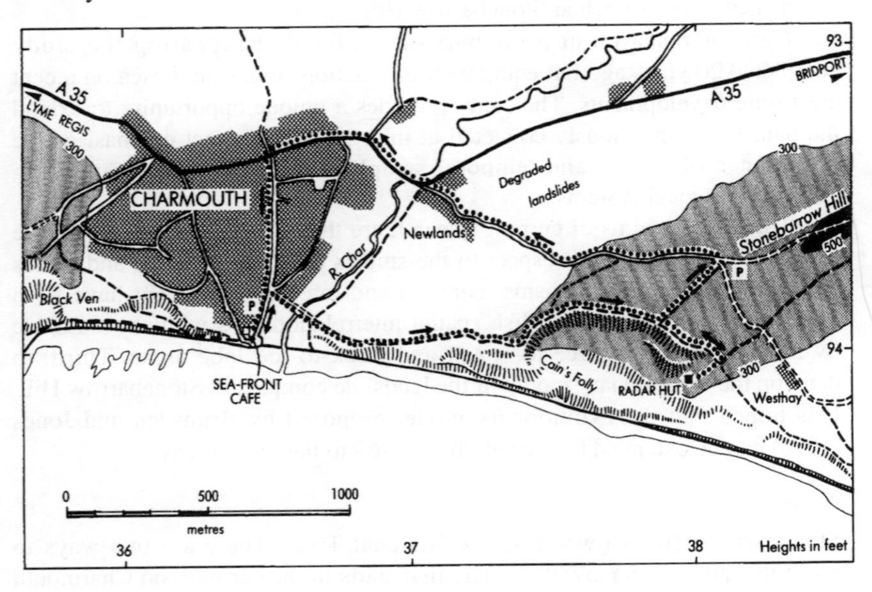

Figure 26. Suggested route for studying Stonebarrow Hill.

At the bottom of the lane a short diversion may be made past the entrance to Newlands caravan park to view the degraded landslides from the A35 road. Undulations are clearly visible in the fields and gravel-filled ditches along the approach to the Charmouth by-pass indicate recent engineering works which have been undertaken in an attempt to stabilise the slope by drainage.

Walk into Charmouth and in the middle of the village turn left down Lower Sea Lane to the sea. Refreshments can be purchased in the centre of the village and, during the summer months, a small cafe adjacent to the sea front car park may be open. Cross the footbridge over the River Char and begin to climb the seaward side of Stonebarrow, using the coastal footpath.

The landslide complex of Fairy Dell soon comes into view and as the summit is approached the entire landslide amphitheatre is revealed. All the zones outlined above can be identified and many of the individual mass movements can be seen. Large rotational slides can be seen stacked up, one behind the other, with the characteristic back-tilt to the original ground surface and towards the seaward edge of the landslide complex extensive mudslide systems are visible. It is dangerous to venture onto the lower slopes at Stonebarrow Hill but if absolutely necessary, it is possible to scramble down to a derelict radar-hut, via a steep path which is strewn with loose rocks and drops over the rear scar towards its eastern end.

The summit of Stonebarrow Hill is an ideal location to view and briefly consider Golden Cap (SY 407923), which at 180m is the highest cliff on the south coast of England.

Landslides are gradually eating back into the summit of Golden Cap. In the centre of the landslide area near vertical cliffs, known as Wear Cliffs, form the junction between land and sea. The basal cliffs are unstable and frequently subject to block detachment while mudslide material is shunted over the cliff edge, plummeting to the beach below. Active coastal erosion keeps the toe of the slope clear of slipped debris as waves constantly attack the base of the cliff during high tides.

On the western flank of Golden Cap is a shallow embayment containing two lines of active rotational slumps. Further to the west, mudslides push lobes of material out across the beach. The mudslides are currently highly mobile. Evidence of past surges remains as boulder arcs which fringe both active and inactive mudslide toe lobes. Behind the mudslides which are shunting debris over the sea cliff at Golden Cap are rotational slumps, with back tilted upper surfaces. Ponds of water are present at the intersection of newly exposed failure scars and the old slipped ground surface.

It is important to note that Golden Cap is somewhat different to the mass movements complexes on Stonebarrow Hill, partly due to the marine erosion at the toe of the slope but also because of a pronounced thickening of the Middle and Upper Lias. The importance of marine erosion emphasises the variation in wave energy distribution along the coast, which increases from west to east reflecting the maximum fetch to the southwest and the coastline wave refraction pattern (Brunsden and Goudie, 1981).

Finally, from the top of Stonebarrow Hill walk away from the sea cliff and toward the car park. A small information centre is occasionally open and is a useful stop for refreshments at the end of the itinerary.

HIGHER SEA LANE

Robert J. Allison

Maps: Ordnance Survey 1:50,000 sheet 193.
Ordnance Survey 1:25,000 sheet SY29/39.
British Geological Survey 1:50,000 sheet 326.

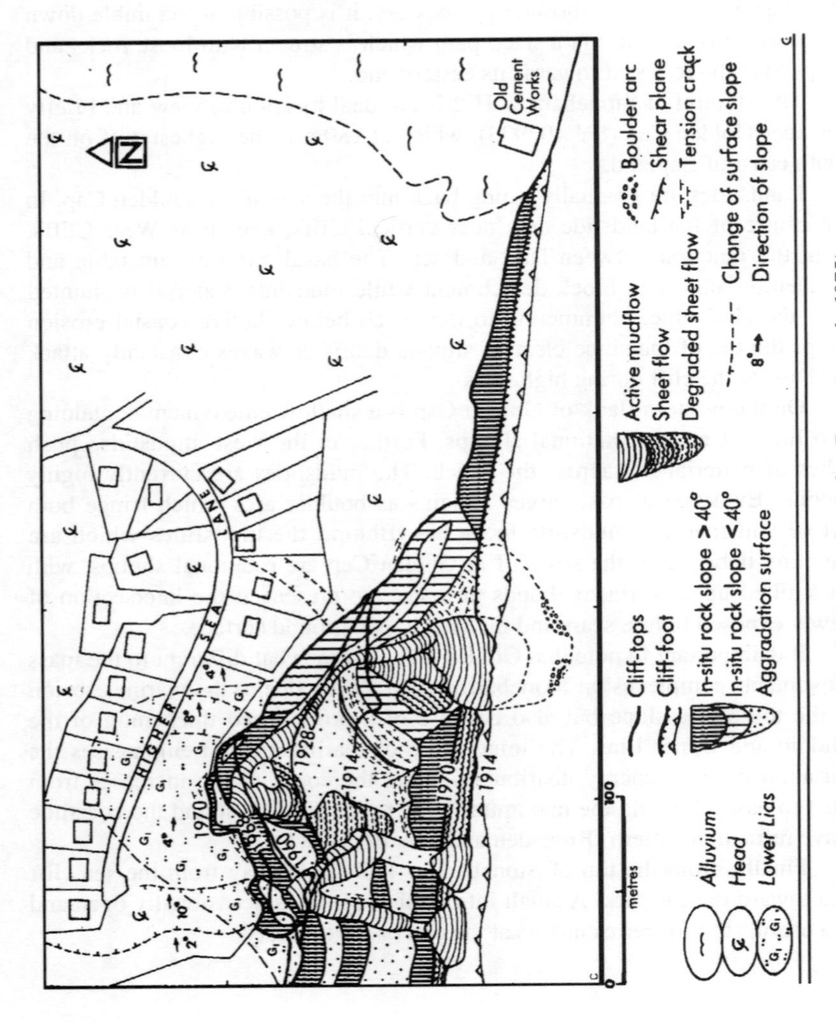

Figure 27. The Higher Sea Lane landslide complex (*after Denness et al., 1975*).

Background History

The mudslides at Higher Sea Lane are situated between the mouth of the River Char (SY 365930) and Black Ven. The most immediate problem at the site is that the coastal landslips, although small and easy to identify, have been receding rapidly towards two rows of houses built adjacent to the cliff (Figure 27). The area of unstable ground is approximately 150m wide and 50m long.

The development of the initial embayment at Higher Sea Lane occurred some time after 1914 and appears to be connected with the presence of an ancient mudflow which moved down the west side of the Char valley, parallel to the present coastline. The ancient mudflow is confirmed by the undulating ground surface to the rear of the sea cliff, which is characteristic of a shallow landslide. When the general pattern of cliff top retreat intersected the margin of the ancient mudflow, a considerable source of water was introduced into the cliff face, partly due to the presence of a nearby spring, partly due to surface water and partly due to water seeping from the base of the Upper Greensand.

The increased water supply resulted in two failures, one in the 1920's and the other in the 1930's and consequently a small mudflow developed, spreading down to and across the beach. A boulder arc today marks the maximum extent of the first mudflow. Following the 1938 event a period of relative stability occurred until 1968, when deep cracks developed in the undercliff and a new mudflow surged out across the beach (Denness et al., 1975).

Higher Sea Lane today

Today the small landslide complex at Higher Sea Lane displays many of the characteristics present in the adjacent large landslide complex at Black Ven (Figure 28). The crest of the stable ground forms an embayment, with the exposed scar being subject to both block detachment and weathering. Tension cracks mark the point where small rotational failures are becoming detached from the land between the landslide complex and the buildings along Higher Sea Lane itself. Dislodged material loads the head of the mudslides, which transport debris down towards the beach. The mudslides pass over terraces and are moving within clearly defined lateral shears, which become lines of running water during wet conditions. The sliding material fans out as it moves down-slope, spreading and falling over a small sea cliff to the beach.

During winter months the moving debris becomes highly saturated. Pools and ponds of water collect across the surface of the disrupted ground and occasionally sheet flow over the sea cliff removes weathered debris,

Figure 28. The landslide complex at Higher Sea Lane.

depositing it on the beach beside and on top of mudslide material. Marine erosion rapidly removes any debris arriving at the toe of the slope and waves cut back into the sea cliff.

A comprehensive geological, geotechnical and geophysical study of the Higher Sea Lane mudslide complex was undertaken by Denness et al. (1975), with a view to stabilising the landslides. The study concluded that the best means of stabilisation was drainage of the adjacent soft, ancient landslide material lying on top of in situ Lias clay, coupled with the grading of the upper cliff to a slope angle of 33° and an artificial superimposed shallow drainage system. The consequent consolidation and stiffening of the unstable soil, coupled with a reduction in the water content of the area around the cliff top, would assist the stabilisation of the cliff. The success of attempts to stabilise the slopes can be examined in the field today.

Access

The Higher Sea Lane landslide complex is easily accessible from the car park at Charmouth sea front (SY 366929) and can be visited en-route to Black Ven or independently, depending on the time available. A public bus service runs through Charmouth and the bus stop, located in the centre of the village, is close to the side road which leads down to the sea.

From the car park access by foot is either along the foreshore in a westerly direction or along the Dorset coastal path, which leaves then car park on the landward side of the sea-front cafe and crosses a field to the small Higher Sea Lane complex.

Suggested Route

Leave the car park on the sea front at Charmouth and walk along the coast in a westerly direction, first along a short break-water which protects a line of huts and then along the beach (Figure 23). The opening into the Higher Sea Lane landslide complex is approached 200m or so along the beach after the end of the break-water.

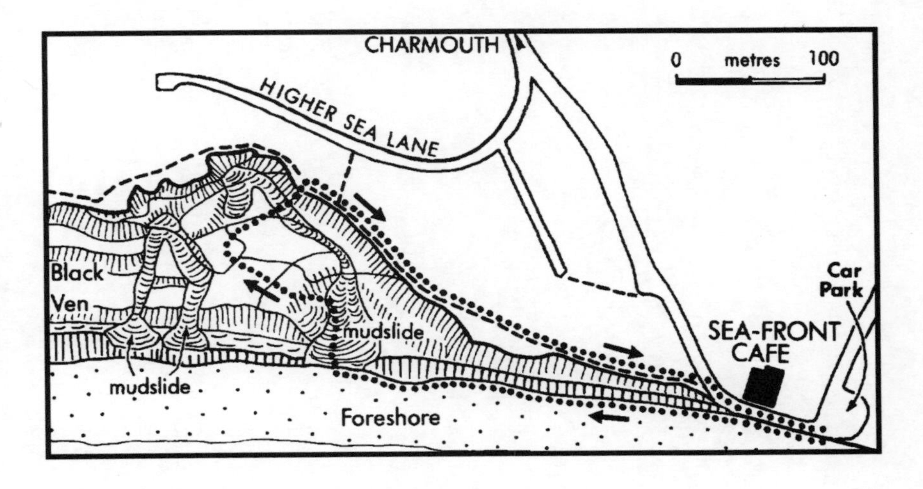

Figure 29. Suggested route for studying Higher Sea Lane.

Walk up into the area of mass movement. Ground conditions are safe even in the wettest of conditions, although old clothes are essential after prolonged rain as the ground becomes particularly muddy. Many of the identifying characteristics of mudslides should be visible. Some time should be spent walking around the hollow which has formed due to landslide activity. It is often possible to identify lateral shears which mark the boundary between stable and unstable conditions. In the winter months reidel shears may be present around the edges of the mudslides due to friction effects between moving and in situ material.

Climb up the back-scar and look back down into the landslide complex. A number of adjacent mudslides can be identified, moving in juxtaposition towards the sea. At low tide it may be possible to see the remnant boulder arc from the 1938 event. The row of bungalows behind the landslide area are along Higher Sea Lane itself. A number of building plots, those closest to the unstable ground, remain undeveloped. It may be possible to see cracks in the exterior walls of some of the bungalows due to subsidence and other ground movements.

For those continuing to Black Ven, return to the beach and continue with the suggested route noted in the next itinerary. Alternatively, return to the car park using the path which crosses the field between Higher Sea Lane and the foreshore cafe.

BLACK VEN

Alexander Koh

Maps: Ordnance Survey 1:50,000 sheet 193.
Ordnance Survey 1:25,000 sheet SY29/39.
British Geological Survey 1:50,000 sheet 326.

Introduction

The Black Ven landslide complex, situated 900m to the west of Charmouth, contains one of the largest systems of landslides in Europe (Figure 30). The area has experienced a long history of instability (Arber, 1941; Brunsden, 1969). It comprises rotational slides, topples, rock falls and slumps of Upper Greensand rock and mudslides, mudflows and sandflows, which feed down to the beach across Liassic materials (see back cover). The current morphology of Black Ven is the result of two significant periods of activity in 1957 to 1958 (Conway, 1974) and 1968 to 1969. Air photographs for 1958, 1969 and 1988 demonstrate in detail the speed with which erosion has occurred.

The original road along the coast from Charmouth to Lyme Regis was destroyed by landslips in the eighteenth century. A cart track running parallel to the road 100m further inland disappeared in 1965 and a section of the heritage coast path collapsed in 1985. Cliff retreat of the order of 5m year^{-1} to 30m year^{-1} is typical during periods of activity. In between major events, erosion at the toe of the slope is around 15m year^{-1} to 40m year^{-1}.

An eye witness to one example of a major debris shunt on 9th and 10th February 1958 (Lang, 1959) wrote:

> *I saw a great mass of Upper Greensand densely covered with bushes and trees slowly crawling downwards from the highest terrace, while below a river of liquid mud was slipping over the low cliff above the beach.... the main movement in the night must have been very rapid, as by daylight a huge fan of debris, crested with uprooted trees, had pushed out beyond the beach to beyond low neap tides.*

The landslides

The Black Ven cliffs reach a height of 145m and are composed of the Shales with Beef, Black Ven Marl and Belemnite Marl of the Lower Lias. These are overlain unconformably by the Gault Clay and the Upper Greensand of the Cretaceous. Dips of 2° to 3° in a south-east to east south-east direction are present in the Jurassic beds. The plane of the unconformity at the base of the Cretaceous dips at angles of 1° to 2° in a south to south

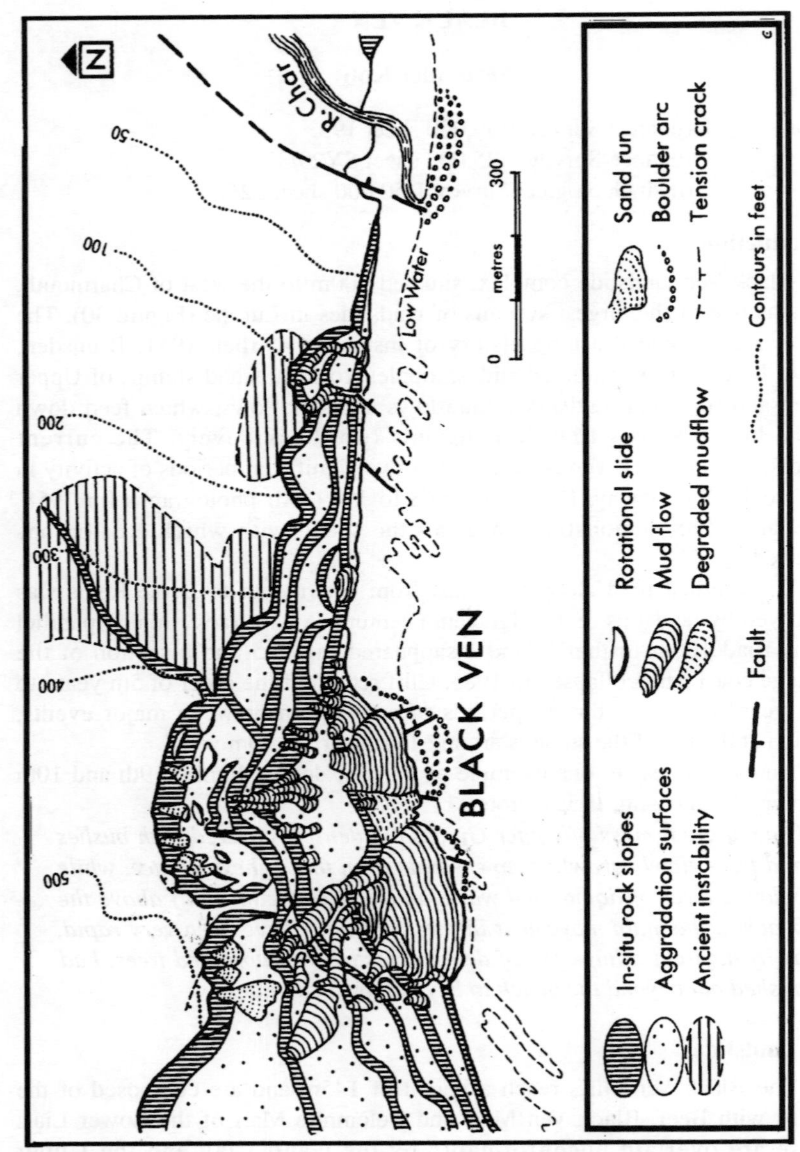

Figure 30. Black Ven (*after Conway, 1974*).

southwest direction. The cliff profile (Figure 31) shows well developed terraces which occur at three main levels, the base of the Upper Greensand, the base of the Belemnite Marl and the base of the Black Ven Marl. Their presence is due to more resistant lithological horizons. Several other minor terraces have developed but they are limited in their spatial extent.

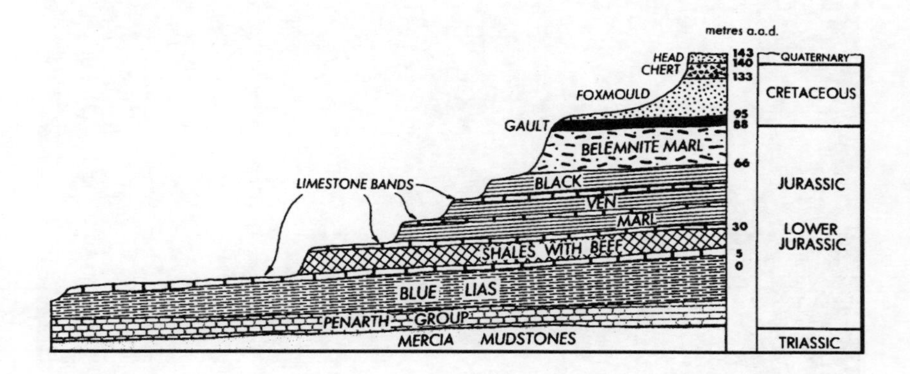

Figure 31. Section through Black Ven *(after Conway, 1974)*.

It is best to consider the Black Ven landslides from the crest to the toe of the slope. The Chert Beds consist of broken chert in a firm coarse sandy clay matrix with some iron oxide cementation in the lower part. They are much harder than the underlying Foxmould, which is a fine, silty decalcified sand. Together the Chert and Foxmould form a steep upper cliff at the rear of the Black Ven mudslides. The cliff is 45m high and capable of generating shear stresses in excess of the shear strength of the decalcified sands. The upper cliffs therefore collapse in single and multiple rotational slides affecting the full thickness of the Upper Greensand. The deposition of iron oxide at the base of the Chert causes partial interception of downward moving groundwater, resulting in the formation of seepage surfaces and springs in the upper cliff face. The seepage surfaces result in deep gullies which cut into the Foxmould.

Undercutting and headward erosion results in the development of conical buttresses between adjacent, deeply incised gullies. Many of the initial failures of sliding blocks occur as a result of the collapse of the buttresses. The gullies sometimes cut down as far as the Gault Clay, which also forms the highest of the three terraces. The supply of water from seepage at the base of the Chert Beds and Foxmould saturates the failed blocks which sit on top of the impermeable, soft, silty and micaceous Gault (Figure 32). When saturated the debris surges forward, a common event during the winter months.

Figure 32. The Black Ven landslides, showing water seepage at the Jurassic Cretaceous unconformity. The most distant cliff marks the edge of the unstable ground and is formed in Cretaceous sediments. The cliff in the foreground is in the Lias.

Accretion ponds develop during winter months on the bench at the top of the Belemnite Marl. Saturated material moves across the bench and drops 20m on to the next terrace at the base of the Belemnite Marl. As a result, the upper cliff looses its toe slope support. The change feeds back to the rear scar, resulting in an increase in the horizontal stresses within the Foxmould, where the cycle of primary instability is repeated. The consequence is the eventual development of new rotational failures at the crest of the landslide complex.

The main cause of material removal in the Belemnite Marl cliff is joint controlled rockfalls, supplemented by erosion and gully formation caused by extensive seepage between the moving debris and the Gault Clay. The rockfall debris, together with material moving from the first terrace higher up the slope, combines to form the sliding debris which passes over the bench developed in the Black Ven Marl. By this stage in the down-slope sequence mudslides and mudflows have developed. The poor hydraulic conductivity of the Black Ven Marl generates increased horizontal groundwater flow between the *in situ* rock and sliding debris. Consequently gullies develop in the winter months and pipes form in the summer. Occasionally the Black Ven Marl is stripped of its surface layer by the moving debris as it advances towards the sea. This results in a steepening of the Black Ven Marl cliff and the generation of high stresses in the clays. The overconsolidated clay absorbs water and swells, shear strength decreases and failure occurs. The debris is funnelled into large mudslide tracks, which pour across the cliff separating the middle and lower terraces (Figure 33).

A similar sequence of events is repeated as material passes over the junction of the Black Ven Marl and the Shales with Beef. A complex depositional area of slides, flows, gullies, pressure ridges and tension cracks develop, coalescing and pushing out towards the sea to form large composite fans and toe lobes.

At times of little or no mudslide activity, the fine material in the toe lobes is washed away to leave boulder arcs on the beach (Figure 34). The degree of saturation of the landslide material has a bearing not only on the velocity of movement but also on the dynamic associations between erosion at the toe of the slope and supply at the head. As movement ceases, the toe lobes become eroded back by the sea to leave boulder arcs along the foreshore. The mudslide surfaces also become vegetated during dry conditions. As the moisture content and pore water pressure of the material increase during a wet phase, the mudslides surge out across the beach. Additionally, flash floods result in mobile and extensive sand runs which cover the main mudslide debris.

Figure 33. Mudslides crossing benches in the Black Ven Marls.

Figure 34. Boulder arcs at the leading edge of mudslides which have surged out across the beach at Black Ven.

Reservoir principle of mass movement and undrained loading

Denness (1971) noted that the geological conditions present at Black Ven are characteristic of the 'reservoir' principle of mass movement. The basic geological requirement for a reservoir is a permeable rock or deposit capable of accepting, retaining and discharging water. The floor of the reservoir must be impermeable or have a permeability significantly lower than that of the reservoir material.

At Black Ven both primary and secondary reservoirs are present. The primary reservoirs are the result of the juxtaposition of *in situ* lithological units of different permeability, particularly where sandy units lie adjacent to sediments with a high silt and clay content. The secondary reservoirs have evolved due to debris accumulations resting on top of terraces which have developed as a result of lithological variations. The ideal conditions for secondary reservoirs are all met at Black Ven. Terraces are wide, almost horizontal and of low permeability, as material weathers particle size is significantly reduced, encouraging maximum water retention, and recession of the cliff terraces is a relatively uniform process.

The dynamic environment of Black Ven also provides an ideal location for testing the undrained loading hypothesis proposed by Hutchinson and Bhandari (1971). The Hutchinson and Bhandari model draws attention to the ability of the lower parts of mudslides to advance by shearing on low angle slopes. In fact undrained loading can result in slip in situations where the slope angle is below the state of limiting equilibrium (Hutchinson, 1970).

By observing pore water pressures in a number of mudslides, Hutchinson found that considerable excess pore water pressures exist in mudslide debris due to loading at the head of the slide as a result of debris falling from the rear scar (Figure 35). In addition to this, Allison (1986) and Allison and Brunsden (1990) have suggested that similar mechanisms operate within individual mudslides as debris shunts down slope. In other words, self loading takes place within the moving mass.

In order to test the Hutchinson and Bhandari (1971) hypothesis instruments were designed, assembled and installed within the Black Ven mudslide system to monitor rainfall, pore water pressure, loading, surface movement and subsurface deformation. Surface movement is conventionally measured by repeatedly surveying markers installed within a mudslide. Recent developments have utilised modified chart drum recorders (Prior and Stephens, 1971) and rotating potentiometers (Allison, 1986; Allison and Brunsden, 1990), in an attempt to obtain continuous movement records.

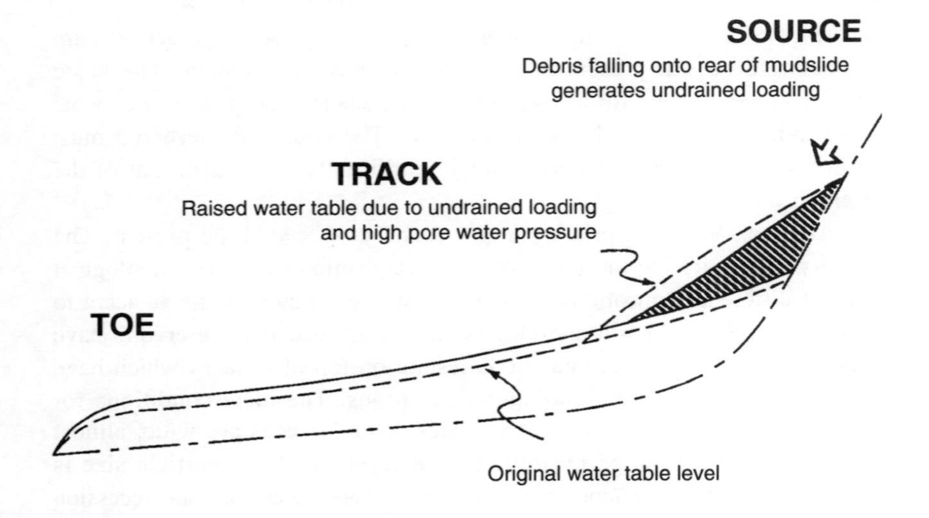

Figure 35. The influence of undrained loading on mudslide pore water pressure *(after Hutchinson & Bhandari, 1971).*

Undrained loading - some preliminary results

Over the last few years the Black Ven mudslide has been monitored using a network of 26 standpipe piezometers, covering the entire length and width of the mudslide system (Figure 36). Site visits every 21 days were used to measure the water level in each standpipe. Each piezometer was also surveyed to obtain data on surface displacements.

An automatic data gathering system configured for rainfall, pore water pressure, loading, surface movement and subsurface displacements at 0.5m vertical intervals was located below the Belemnite Marl cliffs at Black Ven, in order to test the undrained loading hypothesis. Data was collected over 564 days. In total approximately 1.5 million individual recordings were made. A summary of the record is presented in Figure 37. It should be emphasised that these are the preliminary results of data analysis presented on a macroscopic scale.

The initial results show that pore water pressures increased during September 1988, resulting in a large displacement of the instrumented slide. Displacements did not occur after the onset of movement despite the increasing pore water pressures. Several interpretations can be made to explain this behaviour.

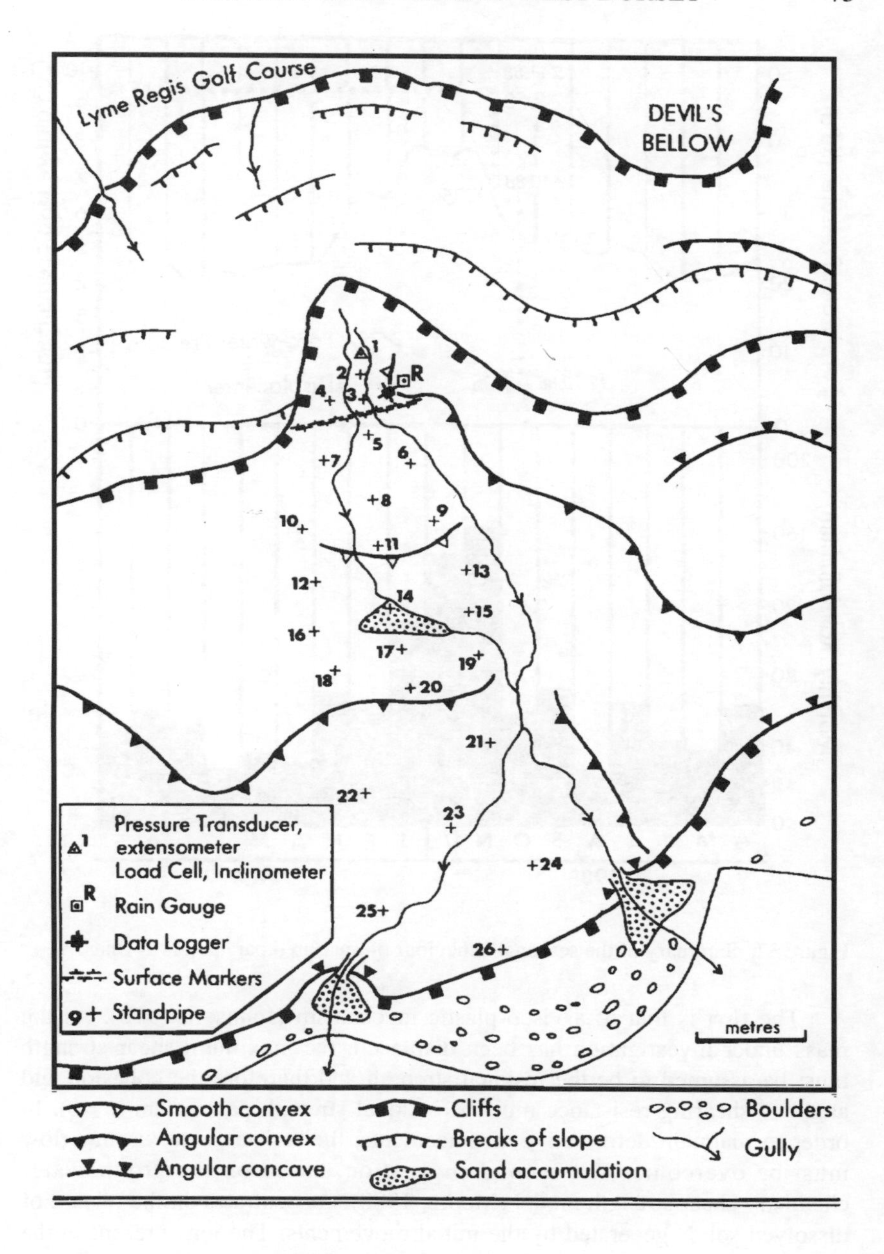

Figure 36. Instrumentation plan for Black Ven.

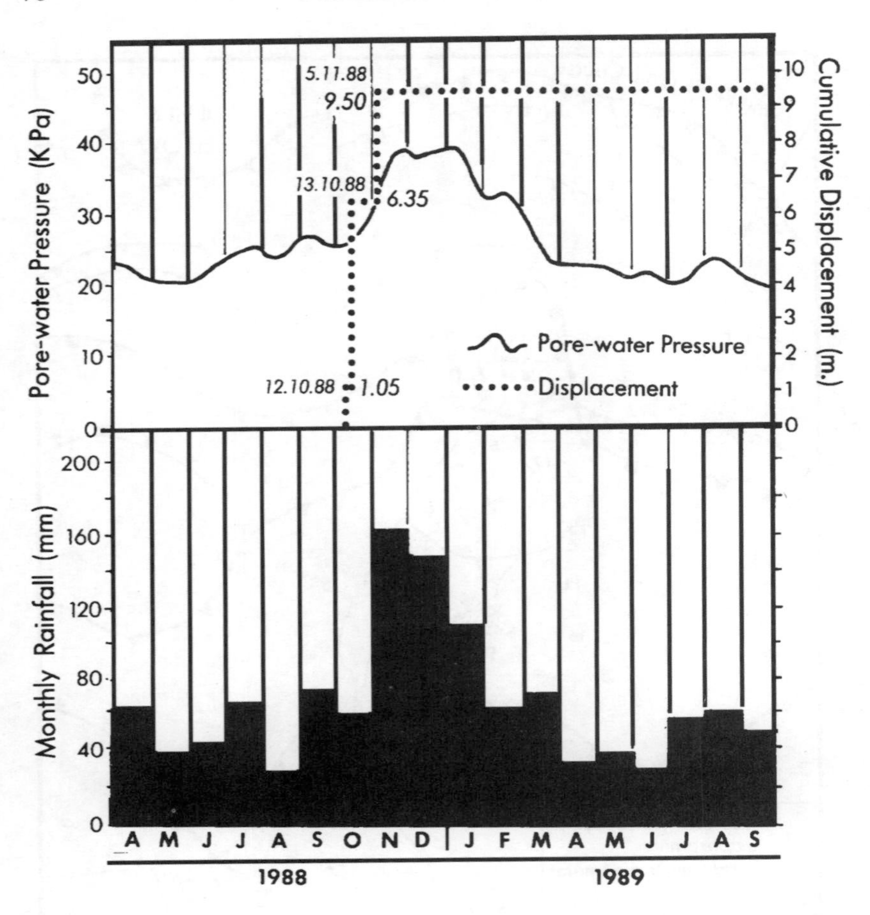

Figure 37. Summary of the seasonal behaviour of measured parameters at Black Ven.

The first is that of a visco-plastic mechanism (Johnson, 1970). As the mass under investigation has been displaced, the maximum shear strength must be assumed to be the residual strength and therefore the cohesion and angle of shearing resistance must be residual strength parameters (c'=0). In order to maintain deformative displacements, the resistance to viscous flow must be overcome. The second suggestion, based on the groundwater chemistry shear strength model (Moore, 1988), concentrates on the release of dissolved solids generated by the initial movements. The ions present in the solutes play an active role in increasing the residual shear strength of the displacing mass by re-establishing the cohesive parameter (bonding due to chemical and electrostatic forces) of the shear strength model. A higher pore water condition is therefore necessary to promote further movement.

Access

Black Ven is owned by the National Trust. There are a number of conveniently located car parks and a selection of footpaths which run to the landslide complex. Each path has restricted access of one sort or another depending on the state of the tide, groundwater conditions and the activity of the slumps, slides and flows. If care is taken Black Ven is quite safe; the fool hardy will run into difficulty.

There are three particularly good access routes, each affording a different site perspective. The first two run from the car park on Charmouth sea front (SY 364931). One follows the beach from Charmouth to Lyme Regis. The other runs up the edge of the cliff, between Lyme Regis Golf Course and the rear scar which has developed in the Upper Cretaceous sediments. The cliff-top route is frequently closed due to landslide activity. It does, however, provide spectacular views over the rotational slides at the rear of Black Ven and is the best location to follow the landslide sequence from the rear scar out into the sea, where boulder arcs are exposed at low tide.

The third route follows a footpath which commences at the car park adjacent to the Charmouth to Lyme Regis road (SY 344928). The path runs approximately north-east, across fields to the upper slopes of The Spittles and through part of the upper Black Ven undercliff. All routes are clearly marked on Ordnance Survey map sheets and sign posted in the field.

Suggested route

The route commences at Charmouth (Figure 38). Cars can be left in a municipal car park on the sea front (SY 364931). Alternatively, a public bus service from Bridport to Lyme Regis runs through the village. If using public transport, alight in the centre of Charmouth and walk down Lower Sea Lane to the sea.

Walk past the small cafe adjacent to the car park, along the sea wall and down onto the beach. The toe lobes of the Black Ven mudslides can be seen pushing out into the sea. The Cobb at Lyme Regis should also be visible. A short distance along the beach is the small landslide complex of Higher Sea Lane (SY 363930). Continue along the shore to the boulders which mark previous seaward limits of the main Black Ven mudslide toe-lobes. The boulder arcs are covered by water at high-tide. At low-water, their arcuate shape is easily identified.

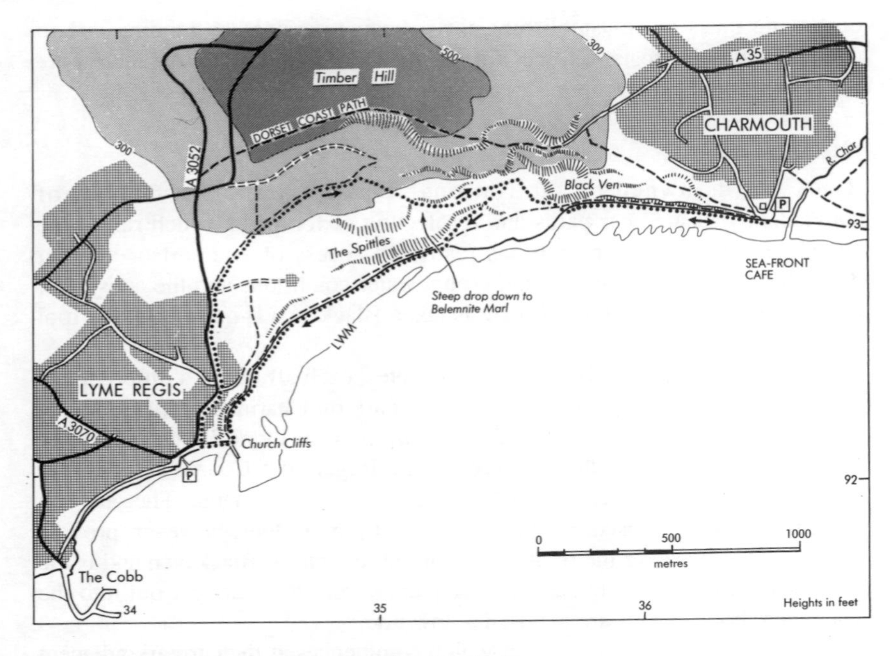

Figure 38. Suggested route for studying Black Ven.

During winter months routes across the surface of the mudslides are difficult to follow. It may be possible to identify tracks which lead onto the lower parts of the slope but do not attempt to break new ground. Conditions under foot can change rapidly and firm conditions one minute degenerate into a quagmire the next. If ground conditions are wet it is best to keep close to or remain on the beach. In dry conditions it is possible to walk up the mudslides, crossing the benches formed by hard limestone bands within the Lias. As the Belemnite Marl cliff is approached the unconformity between the Lias and Upper Cretaceous is visible at the top of the cliff. The former comprises dark grey sediments and the latter yellow and brown materials. Small debris fans front the base of the Belemnite Marl cliff, marking the location of recent falls from the free face and places where debris has shunted over the cliff edge. Many of the identifying characteristics of mudslides can be viewed including the source, track and toe lobe, tension cracks and lateral shears. By turning to face the sea, the juxtaposition of the adjacent mudslides can be seen. This is the best location from which to view the boulder arcs.

Rather than retracing precisely the same route to sea-level it is possible to traverse the benches in the Black Ven Marls before dropping to the beach. Continue along the beach to Lyme Regis. Join the main A 3052 road through Lyme and walk out of town towards Charmouth. As the road climbs away from the sea-front a path leaves its right hand side (SY 344927), traverses two fields and passes onto The Spittles, an extensive area of ground which is disintegrating as a sequence of small translational and rotational block terraces. The Spittles perhaps gives an impression of what Black Ven looked like at an earlier stage in its evolution.

Once on the eastern edge of the broken ground, the path can be picked up again as it passes into coppice woodland which bounds the western edge of Black Ven. The path emerges at a spectacular view point (approximately SY 351931), which looks out over the whole of the Black Ven complex. The Cretaceous back-scar is just visible, with large rotational blocks feeding down to the Belemnite Marl cliff. The Jurassic / Cretaceous unconformity stands out and in wet conditions material may be shunting over the Lias cliff, onto the mudslides which run over the Black Ven Marls. Beyond Charmouth the flank of Stonebarrow Hill is silhouetted on the horizon and, on a clear day, Golden Cap, Thorncombe Beacon and the western end of Chesil Beach all stand out. It may even be possible to identify the yellow cliffs of Bridport Sand at West Bay (SY 462904) and the Isle of Portland on the horizon.

If conditions underfoot are dry, the athletically minded can descend the Belemnite Marl cliff at this point. Care must be taken to identify the best descent route. Once at the bottom of the cliff walk along its base, skirting the vegetation and pass back onto the mudslides. Traverse the lower slopes, return to the beach and walk along the foreshore to the car park at Charmouth. Weather and groundwater conditions frequently prevent this latter part of the route to be followed. There are three alternatives. The first is to re-trace the route back into Lyme, returning along the foreshore to Charmouth. Secondly, there is a good public bus service between Lyme Regis and Charmouth. Thirdly, the Dorset Coast Path, which follows the top of the cliff between Lyme Regis and Charmouth, can be reached by back-tracking through the coppice woodland, crossing the fields which form the up-slope part of The Spittles and walking down the remains of the Old Lyme Road (SY 348934). The path is signposted but be prepared for the route to be closed due to cliff falls.

URBAN LANDSLIDES: IMPACTS AND MANAGEMENT

E. Mark Lee

Maps: Ordnance Survey 1:50,000 sheet 193.
Ordnance Survey 1:25,000 sheet SY29/39.
British Geological Survey 1:50,000 sheet 327.

Introduction

Landsliding is not a hazard that many people associate with Great Britain. Compared with many countries the potential for major destructive landslides is slight and when conspicuous, fast moving failures do occur, they tend to be away from centres of population. The last few decades have witnessed a growing appreciation that landslide features in Great Britain are more widespread and numerous than previously thought. Indeed, a recently completed review recorded 8,835 landslides, with 287 in Dorset alone and 144 of these at the coast.

The landslides of the Dorset coast pose a significant restriction to coastal development and where development already exists, they have resulted in a long history of problems. Man often has a role to play in promoting or renewing slope problems. Landslide management strategies, which have been developed in response to the ever increasing need for an alternative to traditional, hard engineering approaches, have great potential for use along the Dorset coast.

The killer cliffs of Dorset

On Sunday 21st February 1977, a school party studying the geology of Lulworth Cove was buried beneath a sudden rock-slide. Despite rescue attempts by local ambulance men, the teacher and a pupil were killed. Two more pupils were seriously injured, one of whom later died in hospital. At the inquest, the Coroner warned of the dangers posed by the Dorset cliffs and commented on the possibility of a recurrence of the tragedy. The Lulworth incident was not an isolated event. On 28th August 1971 a nine year old girl was hit on the head by a falling rock while walking on the beach at Kimmeridge and later died of her injuries. At Swanage a schoolboy was seriously injured by a rockfall in 1975, a year later another was killed by a falling rock and in 1979 a woman was killed on the beach near Durdle Door when a 3m overhang collapsed.

Tragic though the above events may be, fatalities are a poor measure of landslide hazard as they imply sudden, rapid and unexpected movements which by chance involve humans. Better appreciation of the true cost of landsliding can only be achieved if problems such as damage to roads, railways, pipelines and property, insurance claims, lost property values, transport disruption and delays are taken into account. Few studies have attempted to quantify the cost of coastal landsliding in financial terms, although many local authorities are regularly forced to commit large sums of money towards preventing and stabilising landslides. A recent review of the Dorset coast estimated that an average of £2.5 million is spent each year as a result of coastal slope failures.

An indication of the scale of expenditure commonly associated with landsliding can be gained from the protection works undertaken at West Cliff in West Bay (SY 453908). The development of West Bay coincided with a period of very rapid cliff retreat, at an average rate of 2.5m per year since 1965, resulting in a series of slope associated problems. During February 1978, for example, a rotational slide removed a portion of the Esplanade, requiring nearly £1 million in repair work. The failure was in part attributed to a burst water main discharging into the cliff and the beach immediately in front of the sea-wall. Initially the local authority refused to stabilise the retreating cliffs. However, after a series of slides removed substantial portions of the cliff, West Dorset District Council commissioned a comprehensive coastal protection scheme which included regrading the slope, the installation of drainage and the construction of a sea-wall and promenade at a total cost of over £1 million.

Landslides in Lyme Regis

Particularly serious problems often arise when communities develop on, or expand across ground which is unstable. Throughout Great Britain the occurrence of unexpected slope failures during construction has drawn attention to the widespread existence of a legacy of ancient landslides, now largely concealed by the effects of subsequent slope reprofiling, landscaping and vegetation growth. These features pose threats to many communities, as is the case of Luccombe on the Isle of Wight (Moore et al., 1991), Sandgate in Kent (Palmer, 1991) and parts of the west Dorset coast.

At Lyme Regis, there has been a long history of landslide problems affecting property within the town. Much of Lyme lies on a series of degraded slides developed in Lower Lias clays and overlying head deposits, which mantle the slopes of the River Lim and the coastal cliffs. In the past, the development of parts of the town has resulted in the recurrence of ground instability problems, resulting in damage to property and services. The most problematic area of Lyme Regis comprises the slopes immediately inland of Marine Parade (Figure 39), where landslide movements have been recorded throughout the last 70 years or so (Lang, 1928; Arber, 1941, 1973; Hutchinson, 1962; Pitts, 1979; Strong, 1979; Hawkins, 1991). Lang (1928) and Arber (1941) reported that during the 1920s, small slips periodically

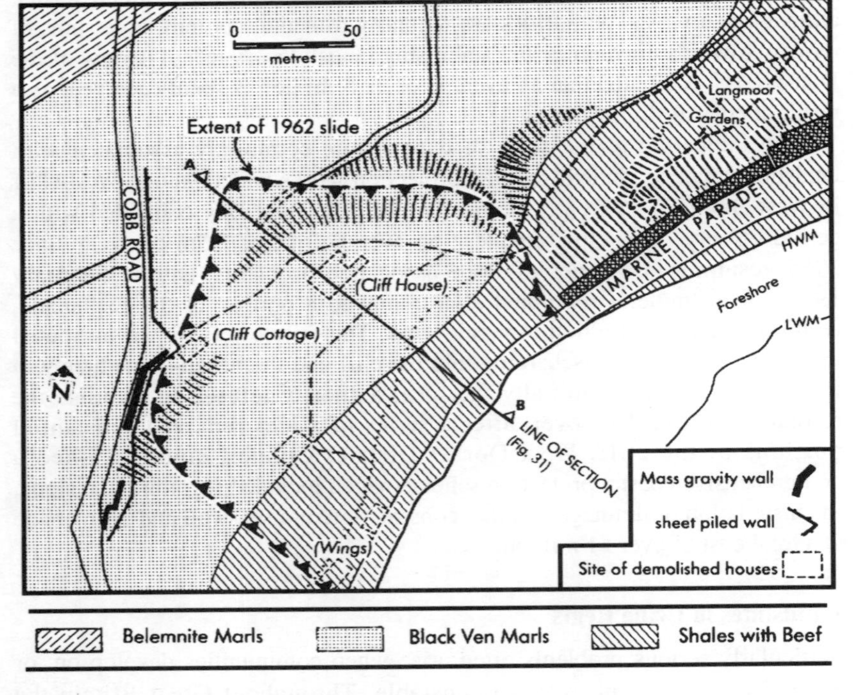

Figure 39. The Marine Parade of Lyme Regis.

occurred in the Langmoor Gardens area, with debris building up behind the masonry wall along Marine Parade. In the winter of 1926-1927, the weight of the debris became so great that the wall failed and material spilled onto the beach. Further slips occurred in 1948 close to Cliff House and cracks developed along Cobb Road. As a result, a 50m long retaining wall was built in 1951 to provide support to the road (Hawkins, 1991). By the 1950s two houses along Cobb Road had become badly damaged by ground movement and had to be demolished. During December 1960 a large, shallow landslide developed on the slope below Cliff House, following a period of heavy rain. A large car park was built in 1961 on the slopes above Cobb Road which soon began to show signs of movement.

The most dramatic movements occurred during the winter of 1961 to 1962 as a result of excavation works on the slopes below Cliff House, associated with the construction of 20 houses and flats. A site investigation identified the shallow failures which had occurred in 1960 and consequently it was proposed to reprofile the lower slopes to a gradient of 33% and install under-drainage. Lyme Regis Borough Council welcomed the proposal (Hutchinson, 1962) as a cure to the persistent slippage onto Marine Parade. Planning permission was granted and around 20,000m^3 of material was removed from the slope. On the morning of 12th February 1962, a few days after the completion of earth moving works, signs of movement were noted in Lister Gardens (Figure 39), together with cracking and heaving in several nearby houses. Movements continued throughout the evening of 12th February and at 9.00 p.m. the whole slope failed, moving several metres in around one minute. Cliff House, which had been standing empty, moved 3.2m towards the sea and back-tilted; (Figure 40) it was demolished later. The nearby Cliff Cottage was tilted more than 10°. The development plans were dropped and a 5m high concrete retaining wall was built along Marine Parade as a remedial measure. The slope was again regraded to a gradient of

Figure 40. Damage to the Cliff House and Cliff Cottage following slope failure.

33% and laid out as a public garden. In addition, a number of trench drains were installed. A 3m to 4m deep perimeter drain and a 150m long sheet-piled retaining structure were also constructed to support Cobb Road which had been affected.

The Lister Gardens slide involved an area of ground 200m by 110m and exposed a circular back scar 5m high. Hutchinson (1962) noted a series of miniature horst-and-graben features within the slide mass, indicating that the failure was probably compound in form (Figure 41). It was later established that the failure had occurred on a pre-existing shear surface within the Shales with Beef and Black Ven Marls, along which intermittent movements had been taking place for decades (Hutchinson, 1984). The initial regrading exercise, which was designed to improve the stability against shallow landsliding, had in fact removed the support from an unsuspected, highly unstable, deeper slide (Hutchinson, 1984).

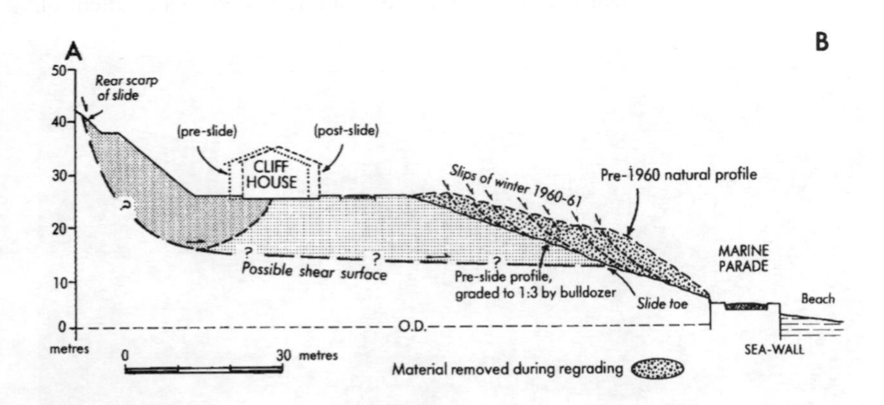

Figure 41. The landslide of February 12th 1962 at Lyme Regis.

Over the last 30 years ground movements have continued to affect the slopes behind Marine Parade in Lyme Regis. In 1971 for example, a mudslide engulfed the rear of a house below Langmoor Gardens. Surface cracking and small slides were reported in 1976, 1978, 1979, 1988 and 1989, a number of which may be related to renewed movement over the deep-seated failure surface. In August 1987, a temporary 7.5 ton weight restriction was imposed along Cobb Road because of renewed cracking to both the highway and adjacent properties (Hawkins, 1991). The whole area still shows signs of slope movement, especially along Cobb Road and in Lister Gardens.

Landslide problems have also been reported elsewhere in Lyme Regis. At Eastcliff for example, significant problems occurred during the 1970s, leading to the demolition of two bungalows. Prior to extensive earth moving operations at the site in 1970, the area had appeared stable (Conway, 1979). As part of the works the surface drainage system was inadvertently disrupted, diverting water into the highly permeable head deposits. This resulted in the reactivation of a degraded mudslide, which quickly spread further up-slope, affecting a larger and larger area. Mudslides have also caused problems on the slopes inland of Monmouth Beach, where a number of holiday chalets have been damaged by run-out in recent years. The same area was affected by mudsliding in 1959, when an RAF Air Sea Rescue Base was partially overwhelmed (Hawkins, 1991).

Man's role in promoting slope failure

The main controls on the initiation of the original landslide activity in the Lyme Regis area were undoubtedly rapid coastal erosion and high groundwater levels during the Flandrian Transgression. This is probably the case for most coastal landslide sites in Great Britain. In Lyme Regis the landslides were probably relatively inactive before the town was built. However, it is likely that development has acted as a destabilising influence on parts of the town. Throughout Lyme Regis development has involved cut-and-fill operations to establish level plots for houses or acceptable gradients for roads and car parks. The 1962 slide in Lister Gardens and the problems at Eastcliff are only the most dramatic consequences of these processes. Elsewhere, the cut-and-fill operations may have promoted local instability problems by changing the surface profile of unstable slopes. The most serious destabilising activity associated with development has probably been the artificial recharge of groundwater levels. Uncontrolled discharge of surface water through soakaways and highway drains may have diverted water into unstable landslide systems, raising groundwater to levels where heavy winter storms could trigger movement. In addition, progressive deterioration and leakage of services such as foul sewers, storm sewers, water mains and service pipes could have added significantly to the problem as has been the case in Ventnor (Lee, Moore, Brunsden and Siddle, 1991) and Luccombe (Moore et al., 1991), Isle of Wight.

It is important not to overlook the impact that over 200 years of coastal modification has had on the stability of inland slopes. The medieval town of Lyme Regis was a major port with shelter provided by a large jetty (The

Cobb) constructed during the 13th century. It was not until 1756 that The Cobb was permanently joined to the coast, preventing easterly long-shore drift. This led to the build-up of trapped coastal sediment material to the west, producing the broad Monmouth Beach and beach shrinkage and erosion below what is now the Marine Parade. The construction of a series of oak groynes in the late 18th century, both at right angles and parallel to the shore, enabled larger quantities of shingle to accumulate below Marine Parade. However much of this material was taken from the beach for construction purposes in the late 19th century. In one year alone about 10,000 tons of shingle was sent to Hull (Woodward, 1985), for example.

By the 1840s the quarrying of rock from the foreshore rock platforms had become an important local industry, supplying the demand for stucco in London. An average quantity of 20,000 tons a year was being removed by 1850, with the result that coastal erosion markedly worsened. Although removal of beach and foreshore material ceased in the early years of this century, the practices are likely to have had an important influence on the stability of slopes by unloading the bottom end of degraded slides and removing the passive support provided by the beach. It is possible that the cumulative effect would have been to progressively reduce the stability of the slopes to a point where renewed movements could occur more frequently.

Landslides as a planning issue

In the past there appears to have been only piecemeal responses to damaging landslide events in Lyme Regis, concentrating on emergency action, repairing buildings and condemning properties damaged beyond repair. There is a need for a more coherent and systematic strategy for dealing with instability problems. Controls on development are gradually being tightened with regard to unstable ground (Department of the Environment, 1990) to minimise the risk and effects of landsliding on property, infrastructure and the public, help ensure that development is not in unstable locations without appropriate precautions being undertaken, bring unstable land back into productive use and assist in safeguarding public and private investment.

The main control over development in Britain is exercised through the planning system. The current legislation is contained in the Town and Country Planning Act 1990, which specifies that no development may be undertaken without planning permission. In the Act, development is defined as the carrying out of building, engineering, mining or any other operations in, on, over or under land, or the making of any material change in the use of any buildings or other land. Some development does not require planning permission, such as the construction of swimming pools. The decision whether or not to grant planning permission must be in accordance with local development plan unless other considerations indicate otherwise. Slope stability is not mentioned specifically in the 1990 Act, although Local Authorities are legally required to draw up development plans which are intended to provide a basis for reviewing planning applications and as a means of coordinating the development needs of an area. In preparing these plans, the local planning authorities are required to undertake surveys which include reviews of the principal physical characteristics of the area and produce a statement on measures for the improvement of the physical environment. In principle, therefore, slopes and their stability could be included as a material planning consideration (Brook, 1991). Indeed, a circular from the Ministry of Housing and Local Government (1961) stated that decisions to permit surface development should not be taken without giving due weight to what is known, or can be conjectured about, the stability of the site. Whilst this advice was directed towards subsidence in coal mining areas, it is clearly applicable to other areas affected by ground instability (Brook, 1991).

The recommended procedures for the handling of planning applications in areas of unstable ground such as Lyme Regis are shown in Figure 42, highlighting the importance of the need for the developer to provide sufficient information to enable the authority to consider the application. It is in the developer's best interest to determine whether a site is on unstable land, as any future movement will affect the value of the site, its development and its maintenance costs. As part of the site investigation the developer should determine whether the land is capable of supporting the loads to be imposed, whether the development will be threatened by unstable slopes and whether the development will initiate slope instability. The local authority must determine whether the development should proceed by taking into account all material considerations, including instability. Even though the local authority may have granted planning permission, the responsibility and subsequent liability for safe development and secure occupancy rests with the developer and landowner. It is widely felt that proper consideration of instability problems in the planning process will assist in reducing the impact of ground movement on communities (Brook, 1991) such as Lyme Regis.

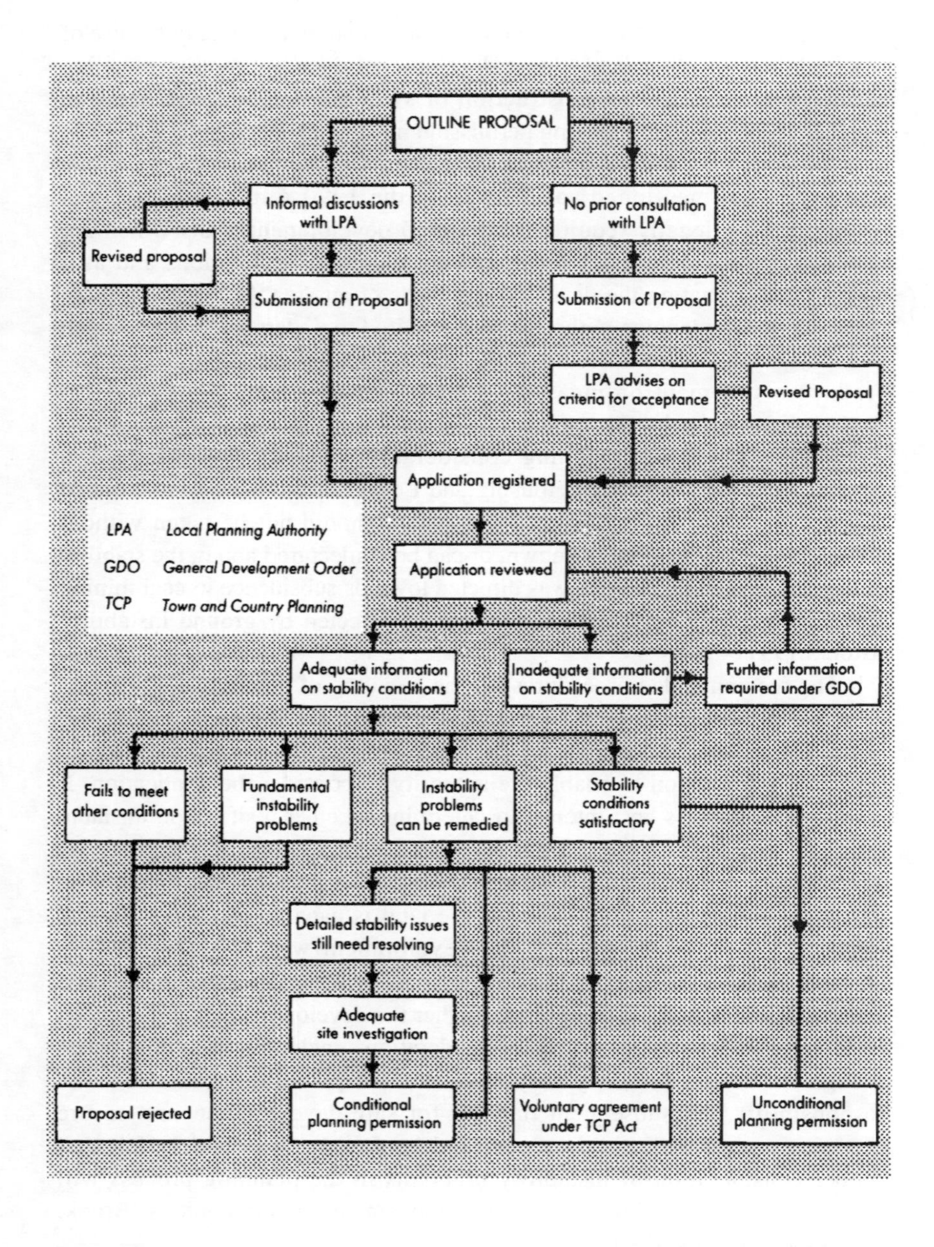

Figure 42. Procedure for reviewing planning applications in areas of unstable land.

Landslide management

One of the most cost-effective ways of integrating landslide information into the planning process is through the production of hazard maps.The basis for this approach is that once identified, landslides or potentially unstable areas can be avoided or developed if appropriate engineering measures are employed. There are many situations where historic development has resulted in the growth of whole communities on what has turned out to be unstable ground. Recourse to large scale engineering works in Lyme Regis could ruin the outstanding coastal scenery that has made the area so popular. Detailed knowledge of the instability problems is required so that pragmatic policies can be developed to reduce risk. This approach has been pioneered by the recently completed detailed study of Ventnor on the Isle of Wight and has led to the formulation of an undercliff management strategy to deal with the problems (Lee, Moore, Brunsden and Siddle, 1991; Lee, Moore, Burt and Brunsden, 1991).

Central to the landslide management approach is the realisation that many of the problems can be reduced if the local community comes to terms with the situation and learns to live with the landslides. A number of issues

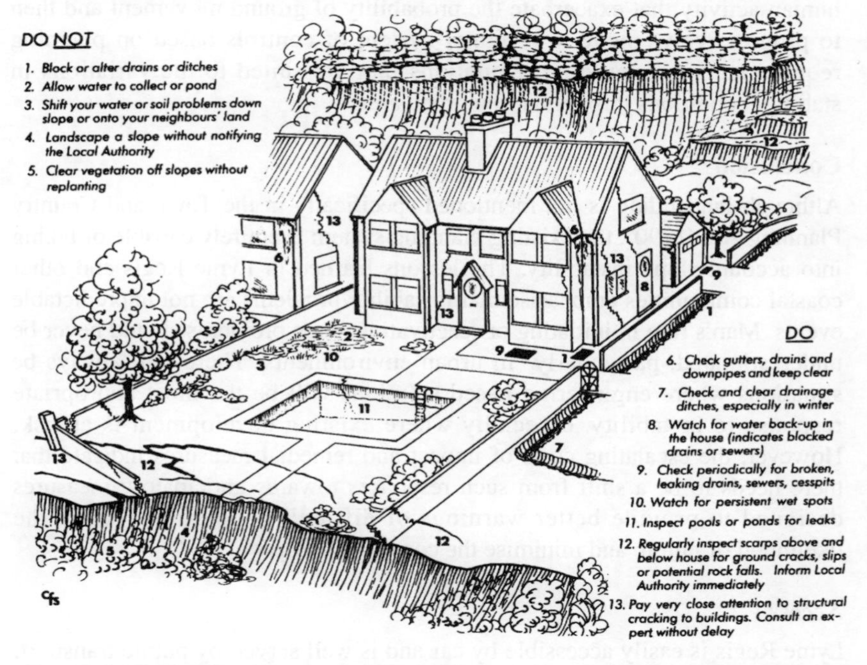

Figure 43. Good maintenance practices for home owners in areas of unstable ground.

are important. First, control of construction activity with particular emphasis on avoiding inappropriate cut and fill operations and timing of earth movement operations. Second, preventing water leakage from water mains, services and sewers. Soakaways, French drains and other natural percolation methods of surface water should be avoided. The importance of preventing water leakage is often likely ot be amongst the most cost-effective way of reducing the likelihood of damaging ground movement events. Third, improved building standards are necessary. Many buildings situated on slow-moving landslides are of unsuitable construction and are readily damaged by ground movement. While solutions to the problems of unstable ground have long been practised in coal mining areas, there appears to have been no attempt to accommodate movement in the design or construction of property in Lyme Regis. Finally, good maintenance by individual home owners is essential. Neglect can result in localised instability problems (Figure 43).

These proposals are essentially pragmatic. Recourse to large scale, conspicuous, engineering works such as toe weighting and coastal defences would probably be unacceptable in Lyme Regis, which is dependent on tourism. Coordinated measures need to be taken, first to limit the impacts of human activity that exacerbate the probability of ground movement and then to progressively move to a tighter system of controls based on planning requirements and building regulations that are suited to the variations in stability conditions throughout the urban area.

Conclusion

Although landsliding is not mentioned specifically in the Town and Country Planning Act (1990), the existing planning system is entirely capable of taking into account slope instability. The lessons learned in Lyme Regis and other coastal communities emphasise that instability problems are not unpredictable events. Man's role in initiating or reactivating slope problems should never be underestimated, particularly in urban environments. There will always be situations where engineering based solutions will be the most appropriate response to instability, especially where existing development is at risk. However, the escalating costs of impact and remedial measures indicate that there needs to be a shift from such responses towards anticipatory measures designed to provide better warnings of difficult conditions, reduce the likelihood of failure and minimise the consequent impact.

Access

Lyme Regis is easily accessible by car and is well served by public transport. The A3052 road runs through Lyme in an approximate east to west direction and the A3070 road comes into the town centre from the north. A public bus service runs through the town between Axminster and Bridport. There are two large public car parks, one on either side of the town.

If arriving in Lyme Regis by car from the east, the A3052 road is signposted shortly after the Charmouth by-pass. As the A3052 road drops down into the town centre, a car park is approached on the left hand side of the road (SY 344927). From the west, a car park is located on the right hand side of the road (SY 336919) just before the final descent to the main street. A small car park is located in the centre of the town close to the Lyme Regis museum but it is small and spaces are seldom vacant. All three car parks are clearly signposted.

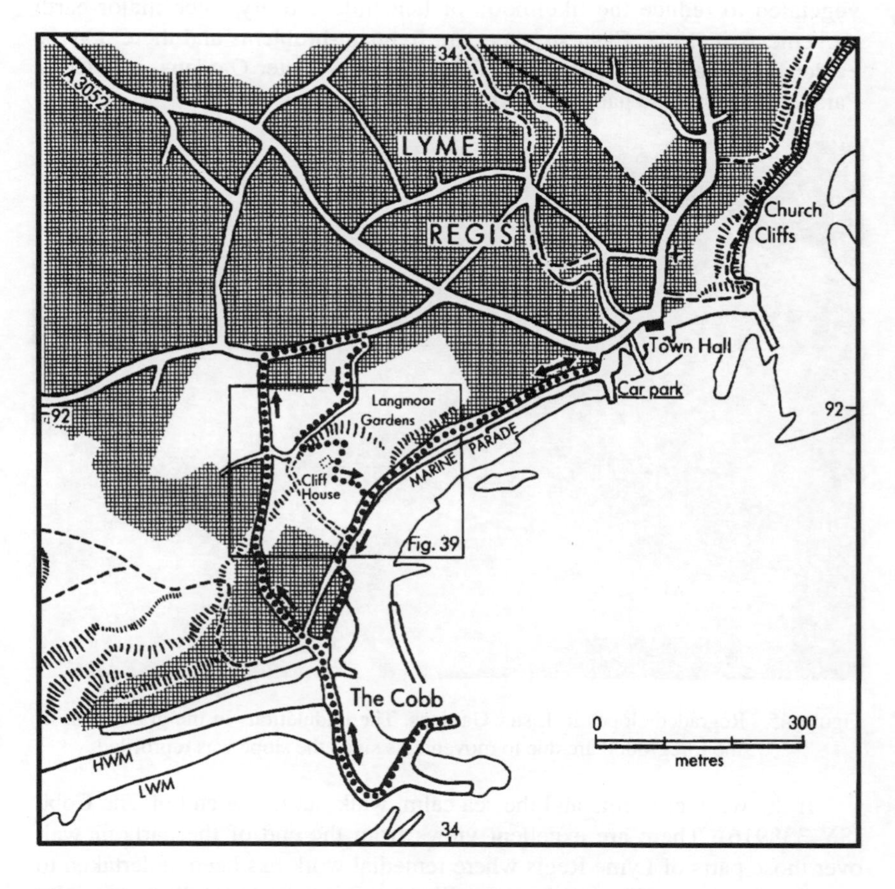

Figure 44. Suggested route for studying the urban landslide problem in Lyme.

Suggested route

The route (Figure 44) commences in the car park at the centre of Lyme Regis (SY 343921) and is one of the best walks for examining the effects of landsliding on an urban area. Walk along Marine Parade to the end of the row of shops, towards the small harbour and The Cobb (SY 338916). A 50m long retaining wall along Marine Parade has been built as one of a number of remedial measures adopted in an attempt to halt ground movements.

Lister Gardens are adjacent to Marine Parade beyond the shops and represent the most problematic area of Lyme Regis in terms of unstable ground. Numerous landslide movements have been recorded over the last 70 years (Figure 45). The whole of Lister Gardens has been reprofiled, landscaped and vegetated to reduce the likelihood of landslide activity since major earth movements in 1962. Even so, there are frequent problems and there may be evidence of cracking along the wall which fronts Lister Gardens, on Marine Parade and along the paths which traverse the Gardens.

Figure 45. Regraded slopes in Lister Gardens. The undulations in the grass bank in the foreground are due to movements since the slope was reprofiled.

If the weather is fine and the sea calm, walk out to the end of The Cobb (SY 338916). There are excellent views from the end of the harbour wall over those parts of Lyme Regis where remedial work has been undertaken to stabilise the slopes. The whole area still shows signs of instability, especially along Cobb Road and in Lister Gardens. From the end of The Cobb on a fine day, there are excellent views to the east past the landslides of Black Ven (SY 355929) and Stonebarrow Hill (SY 375927). Similarly, to the west, the landslides of Ware Cliffs (SY 325910), Pinhay Bay (SY 320907) and the Axmouth - Lyme Regis National Nature Reserve can be viewed across the county boundary in Devon.

Walk back along The Cobb to the shore and up the steep incline of Cobb Road. The remains of houses are passed on the right hand side. The buildings had to be demolished following ground movement in the 1960s, highlighting the importance of landslide activity and the destabilising effects on local property.

The car park at the top of Cobb Road is another area of ground which is affected by movement. On a number of occasions since the car park was originally laid out in the 1960s movement has resulted in cracking of the ground surface. At the junction of Cobb Road and the A3052 turn right and walk down hill back into the centre of Lyme Regis and the car park. Alternatively, walk a short distance down the hill and turn right into Langmoor Gardens. The entrance is clearly signposted. The Gardens represent another area of ground that has been reprofiled and drained in an attempt to improve the stability of the ground. Walk along the paths through the gardens, down on to Marine Parade and from there back along to the car park in the centre of Lyme.

COASTAL SEDIMENT SUPPLY AND TRANSPORT

Malcolm J. Bray

Maps: Ordnance Survey 1:50,000 sheets 193,194.
Ordnance Survey 1:25,000 sheets SY29/39, SY49/59, SY58, SY68/78, SY67/77.
British Geological Survey 1:50,000 sheets 327, 342.

Introduction

The west Dorset coast is protected by a presently discontinuous sequence of shingle beaches, of which Chesil Beach (SY 605810) is the most extensive. A critical difference in the nature of the coast east and west of West Bay (SY 462904) results from the degree of protection afforded by the shingle beaches. The substantial Chesil Beach almost completely protects the land behind, so cliffs only exist close to West Bay where the beach is lower. To the west, the beaches offer only partial protection and major landslide systems have developed on the rapidly eroding coast.

Although Chesil is believed to be a fossil feature receiving little or no shingle input at present (Carr, 1980), the adjacent coast between West Bay and Lyme Regis remains highly active in terms of shingle movement. Previous studies along the west Dorset coast have concentrated on either beach processes (Carr 1969, 1971, for example) or landslide processes (Brunsden and Jones, 1976, 1980, for example). It has consequently been difficult to understand the behaviour of the nearshore coastal sediment system and impossible to verify whether or not Chesil Beach is a relict landform. The possibility of linkage between the relatively stable Chesil Beach and the dynamic, eroding coast to the west has been widely discussed (Brunsden and Goudie, 1981) but has only recently been the subject of detailed research.

Landslides and littoral zone sediment budget

Sediment circulation has been analyzed between Lyme Regis and West Bay in an attempt to elucidate sediment supply and transport processes close to and on both sides of the shore. Research has thus integrated studies on the landward and the seaward sides of the high-water level. Attention has been focused on three pocket beaches at Charmouth (SY 366929), Seatown (SY 420916) and Eype (SY 448910) (Bird, 1989). Their separate identity arises due to landslide debris, which has surged out beyond the base of the cliff at points along the coast. The major sediment inputs, transfers, outputs and stores comprising the west Dorset coastal system are outlined in Figure 46. Attention is focused on gravel (greater than 2mm diameter clasts) which comprises the bulk of the beach material.

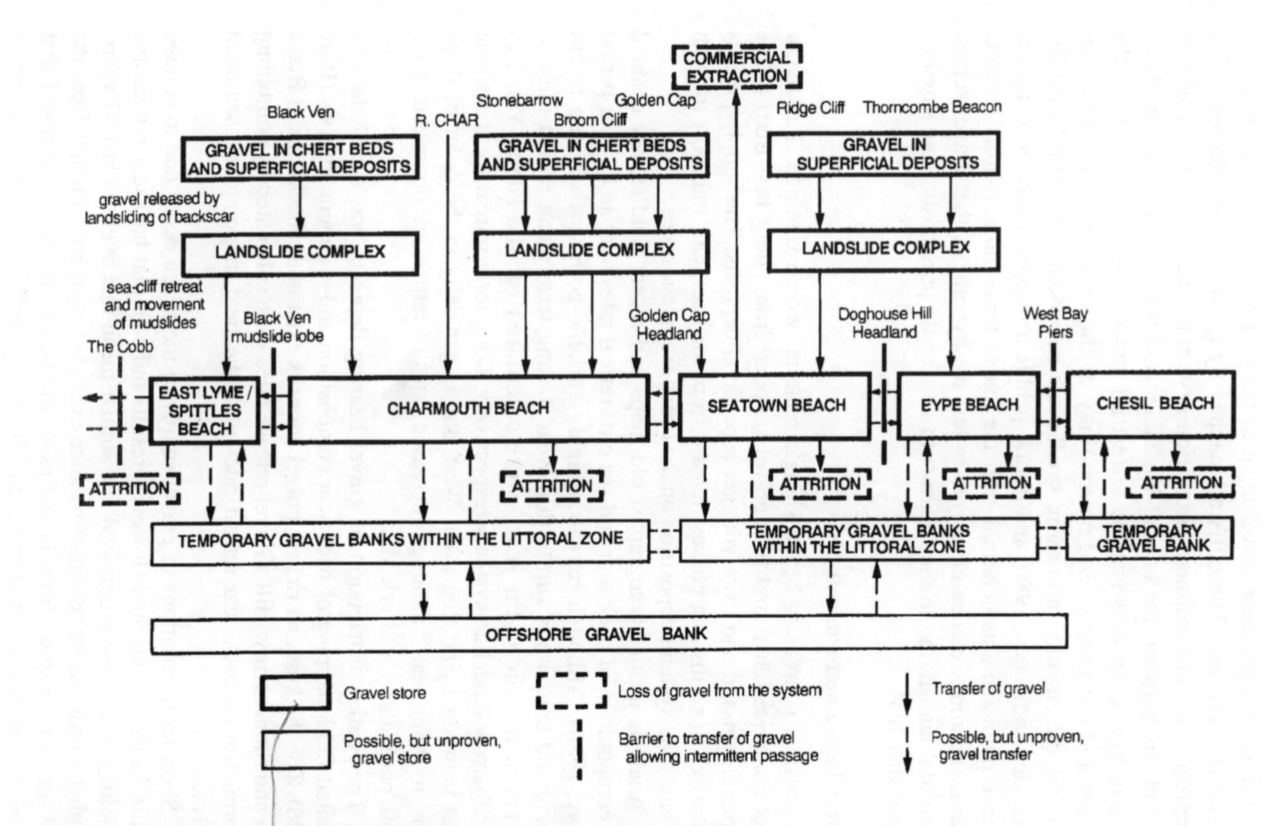

Figure 46. Model of the gravel supply from coastal landsliding.

The most significant gravel input to the nearshore zone is provided by coastal cliff erosion. The cliffs are capped by gravel-bearing deposits. The complete nearshore sediment circulation system is characterised by complex interactions between the coastal landslides and the littoral zone. Feedback relationships exist between the terrestrial and marine components of the system and the process and morphology of the two are interrelated. For example, the chaotic, short-term, small scale behaviour of coastal landslides (Brunsden and Jones, 1980) and littoral pebble transport (Carr, 1971) appear to have predictable associations over the longer term and at a broader scale. Such associations can be employed to test the hypothesis that gravel supply by coastal landsliding in the Charmouth area could previously have supplied Chesil Beach.

Littoral zone material supply

All possible sources of beach shingle material were examined. The major input comprises chert and flint gravel supplied from the Chert Beds of the Upper Greensand and from younger superficial deposits. The supply process comprises three distinct phases: release from the backscar; transport through the landslide system; deposition on the beach from landslides.

Analysis of air photographs, old maps and recent field survey enabled the computation of back scar and sea cliff retreat rates over an 87 year period (Bray, 1986). Although retreat is highly variable both spatially (up to 5m $year^{-1}$) and temporally (up to 20m $year^{-1}$), long term mean retreat rates of 0.71m $year^{-1}$ and 0.4m $year^{-1}$ were calculated for the Black Ven and Stonebarrow landslide systems respectively. Long term retreat for the whole coast between Lyme Regis and West Bay is generally in the order of 0.3m $year^{-1}$ to 0.5m $year^{-1}$, although increased rates of retreat are noticeable since 1960, particularly at Black Ven.

The spatial distribution of gravel bearing deposits was established by detailed field mapping of back scar composition and sediment analysis (Bray 1986). The thickest and richest gravel deposits exist in the backscars at Black Ven and Stonebarrow Hill. Gravel release rates were calculated by combining information on back scar retreat rates with the field mapping and sediment analysis.

Short term variations in gravel supply to the beach occur due to storage within landslide systems. However, results indicate that backscar retreat and sea-cliff retreat have progressed at a similar mean rate over the last 87 years. In other words, an approximate balance exists between gravel inputs from the backscar and outputs from landslips to the beach. It should be noted that during the study presented here, only 50% of gravel released by rapid retreat at Black Ven since 1957 has reached the beach. A further 15 to 20 years of rapid supply are probably required for equilibrium to be established. The supply of gravel to the beaches (Figure 47) is concentrated between Lyme Regis and Golden Cap, with 80% to 90% coming from the Black Ven and Stonebarrow landslides. Total gravel supply from coastal erosion is estimated to have been 4650m^3 year^{-1} between 1901 and 1988. The supply should increase in the near future as large volumes of material within the Black Ven landslide systems reach the coast. A long term supply volume of 5600m^3 year^{-1} has been calculated.

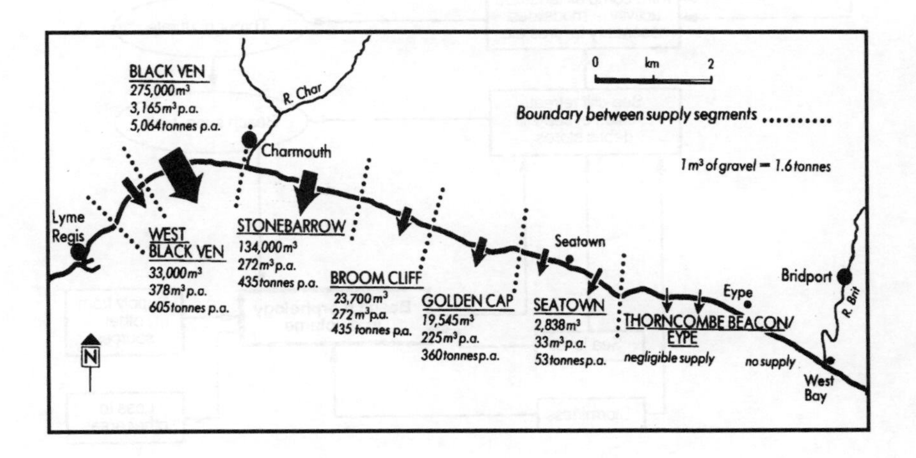

Figure 47. Coastal erosion gravel supply in west Dorset coast, 1901-1988.

The gravel supply process is represented in Figure 48. Supply is regulated by landslide mechanisms. The landslide systems resist change by negative feedbacks which act as a 'damping' mechanism. An example is as follows. Increased sea cliff erosion promotes landslide activity within the undercliff. The backscar is consequently unloaded, resulting in the development of a major rotational slide. The rotational slide releases additional material to the undercliff and thence to the beach. As a result, greater protection against marine erosion is afforded to the toe of the landslide area, slowing sea cliff retreat and reducing activity in the undercliff.

The landslides along the west Dorset coast can therefore be considered in terms of a flow of materials from backscar to foreshore. If all particle size grades are considered (Table 2) only 2% of the total is gravel. Coastal slope stability drops if the greater than 2mm size fraction is removed from the toe

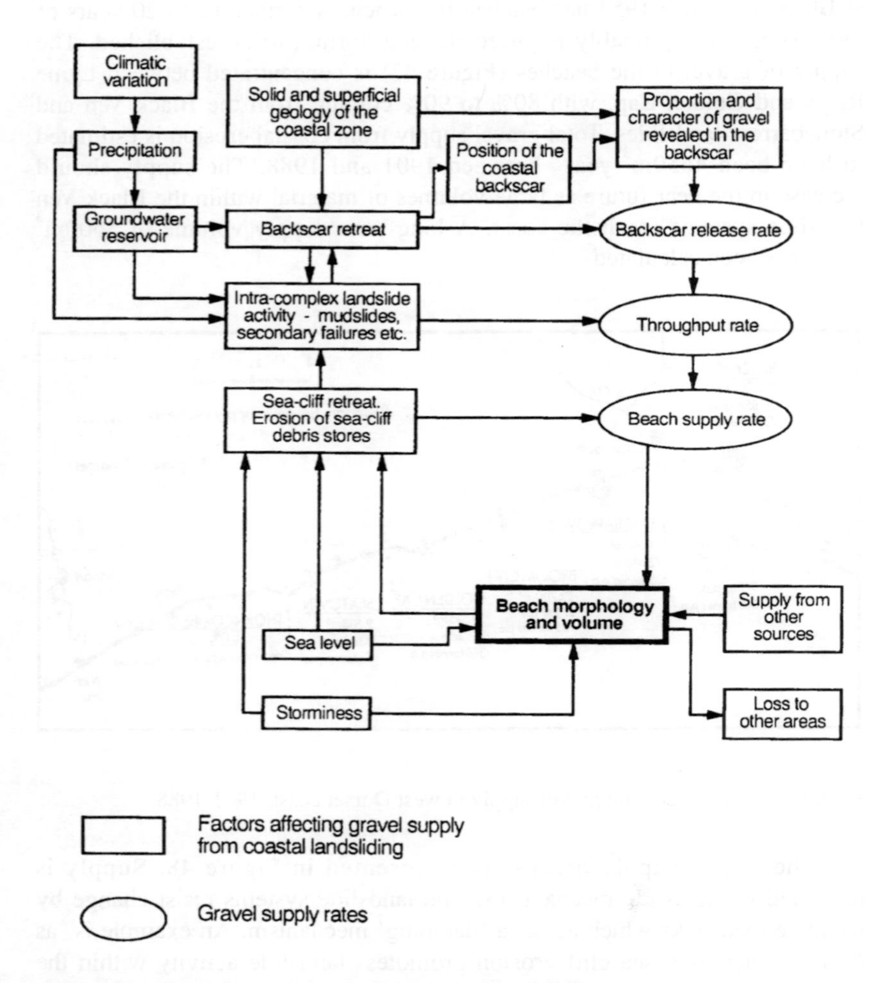

Figure 48. Model of gravel supply from coastal landsliding.

of the slope. The material is critical to slope stability, remaining on the foreshore as a protective barrier, whilst the sand, silt and clay are easily eroded. If marine erosion is great a stable slope can not form. At most points along the coast erosion exceeds sediment supply; fine sediment is transported offshore and shingle beaches develop. At the toe of very active landslide systems supply temporarily exceeds toe slope erosion. Sediment accumulates on the foreshore in the form of mudslide lobes, interrupting surf zone

Table 2. Release of all material types, 1901-1988.

Material Type	Lyme Regis-R. Char		R. Char-Golden Cap		Golden Cap-Eype		Total	
	m^3	%	m^3	%	m^3	%	m^3	%
Gravel	308,241	2.1	177,236	2.0	2,838	0.1	488,315	1.9
Limestone	635,883	4.3	127,716	1.4	21,924	0.9	758,523	3.0
Sand	1,635,078	11.1	1,450,812	16.0	1,173,456	48.5	4,259,346	16.2
Clay	12,122,928	82.5	7,287,207	80.6	1,220,697	50.0	20,630,832	78.9
Total	**14,702,130**		**9,042,971**		**2,481,915**		**26,164,016**	

sediment transport. The result is increasing depletion of shingle down-drift of the lobe. It can be tentatively suggested that where shingle accumulations increase, landslide activity is reduced due to better toe slope protection (Jones and Williams, 1991). Where shingle is depleted, toe slope protection is reduced and consequently landslide activity increases. If this is correct, zones of active landsliding will migrate in the direction of longshore drift. This sort of process may well have contributed to the eastward migration of intense landsliding at the Spittles between 1900 and 1930 to the central region of Black Ven by the late 1950's.

Littoral zone shingle transport

Although gravel supply to the beach is concentrated at Black Ven and Stonebarrow, shingle volume increases eastward on each beach, suggesting a net eastward littoral drift. A detailed assessment of longshore drift has been conducted by examining the beach deposits and undertaking tracer studies (Bray, 1990).

Analysis of 12,000 beach pebbles across a total of 14 transects on Charmouth, Seatown and Eype beaches revealed that pebble lithology and size distribution are similar on all of the west Dorset beaches including Chesil Beach. Pebble roundness and sphericity increase to the east, suggesting littoral drift from the west within the study area. The beach pebbles are of similar lithology and size range to gravel supplied to the coast by landslides. Clast roundness and sphericity is greater at sea level due to marine sorting and attrition. Results suggest that the west Dorset beaches were previously connected, with a common shingle source. Pebble size, sphericity and roundness gradings indicate net eastward littoral drift on Charmouth beach, slight net eastward drift on Seatown beach and no clear drift direction on Eype beach.

Littoral drift was measured directly by a series of experiments employing aluminium tracer pebbles. The tracers were efficiently recovered to a maximum depth of 0.45m beneath the beach surface using metal detectors. Recovery rates approaching 100% were achieved. Tests were conducted simultaneously on shingle (St Gabriel's) and mixed sand and shingle (Charmouth) beaches during high and low wave energy conditions. The data were analyzed using multivariate techniques. Results indicate that shingle transport is most rapid on the upper beach near the high water mark. The larger tracers were the most rapidly transported. The observed increase in pebble size from Charmouth to Golden Cap could therefore have developed by eastward littoral drift. Longshore transport volumes were calculated from the velocity, thickness and width of the moving shingle layer. The volumes were $2m^3$ day^{-1} to $22m^3$ day^{-1} during frequent periods of low wave energy westward drift, increasing to a maximum of $168m^3$ day^{-1} during less frequent periods of high wave energy eastward drift. Comparison of results with a representative wave climate for West Bay over a 10 year period (Hydraulics Research Station, 1985) indicates a net eastward drift of $3447m^3$ $year^{-1}$ at St Gabriel's. Calibrated wave power equations were produced to aid shingle transport prediction at the two sites.

At Charmouth, net eastward drift is estimated at $4710m^3$ $year^{-1}$ but 40% of the material is composed of sand and grit; shingle drift is $2825m^3$ $year^{-1}$. Drift of the entire beach sediment size spectrum decreases towards the east due to the progressive offshore loss of fines.

Beach sediment budget analysis

Gravel budgets were calculated for Charmouth, Seatown and Eype beaches. The Charmouth beach system was examined in detail because it is the most dynamic and receives the biggest input from coastal landslides. Removal of gravel from the beach by offshore transport was initially assumed to be negligible, as suggested by the tracer experiments and sea floor sampling. Other gravel outputs from the beach by attrition and entrapment are comparatively small. Substantial beach accretion at Charmouth should have occurred since 1901. This is not supported by the comparison of old maps, field reports and the contemporary volume of the beach. The imbalance can be explained by intermittent phases of eastward littoral drift beneath Golden Cap. Old photographs show that landslide debris blocking the foreshore beneath Golden Cap became sufficiently eroded between 1934 and 1949 to allow a continuous beach to exist from Charmouth to Seatown. Observations along the west Dorset coast indicate that mudslides evolve by active phases of surging, separated by long phases of low activity. The barriers formed by the landslides are thus liable to retreat. The process described above was recently observed at Black Ven. The cessation of major mudslide surges in 1984 allowed erosion of the toe lobe and a small beach evolved in November 1988.

During periods when a continuous beach is established beneath Golden Cap the headland operates as a one way valve. All sediment drift is in an eastward direction. The analysis of shoreline orientation and dominant wave approach directions indicates that westward drift is minimal (Hydraulics Research Station, 1985).

The flow of gravel through the Charmouth beach system (Figure 49) demonstrates a number of points. Supply is concentrated in the western part of the beach. Net transport is to the east and consequently the western part of the beach is subject to depletion despite its proximity to supply. Accretion is concentrated on the eastern part of the beach, explaining the eastward increase in beach volume. Shingle transport to Seatown beach is possible although supply is intermittent due to landsliding at Golden Cap.

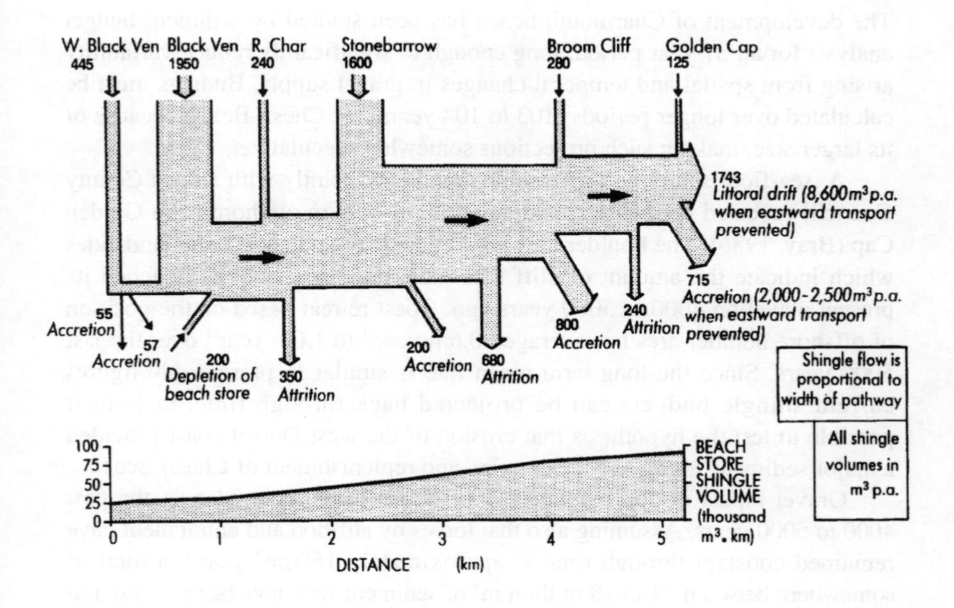

Figure 49. Gravel flow through Charmouth beach.

The spatial distribution of coastal landslide sediment inputs and beach accretion are important regulators of beach and landslide dynamics. Beach accretion provides protection to the base of the sea-cliffs. If retreat rates slow down, gravel supply is reduced, accretion is limited and increased marine erosion facilitated. The idealised negative feedback mechanism cannot operate efficiently on Charmouth beach because eastward littoral drift prevents shingle accretion on the foreshore beneath the major landslide supply areas. The western part of the beach system is therefore characterised by high sediment throughput and relatively low volumes of shingle. No material is sufficiently stable on the western part of Charmouth beach to provide long term protection to the base of the cliffs. Clay and sand are supplied in large quantities but are easily eroded and transported offshore. Limestone boulders, chert and flint gravel provide only temporary protection because of the low durability of the former and the potential for longshore transport of the latter. The active phase of landsliding initiated at Black Ven in the late 1950's is therefore likely to continue because natural basal protection is unlikely to keep pace without increased landslide throughput.

Coastline evolution

The development of Charmouth beach has been studied by sediment budget analysis for an 87 year period, long enough to significantly reduce variability arising from spatial and temporal changes in gravel supply. Budgets must be calculated over longer periods (103 to 104 years) for Chesil Beach because of its larger size, making such projections somewhat speculative.

A sea-floor sampling programme (conducted jointly with Dorset County Council) revealed boulder arcs extending 3km to 4km offshore from Golden Cap (Bray, 1986). The boulder arcs are remnants of ancient coastal landslides which indicate the amount of cliff recession since sea level approached its present elevation 4000 to 5000 years ago. Coast retreat based on the position of offshore boulder arcs has averaged 0.6m $year^{-1}$ to 1.0m $year^{-1}$ over the last 5000 years. Since the long term mean rate is similar to present day figures current shingle budgets can be projected back through time, making it possible to test the hypothesis that erosion of the west Dorset coast provided a major sediment source for the creation and replenishment of Chesil Beach.

Gravel inputs of approximately 5000 $year^{-1}$ have occurred over the past 4000 to 5000 years. Assuming also that losses by attrition and entrapment have remained constant through time at approximately 1500m^3 $year^{-1}$, a total of somewhere between 14 to 18 million m^3 of sediment will have been released to the coast by landslides since 5000 B.P. Present day shingle storage between Lyme Regis and West Bay is estimated at slightly less than 1 million m^3.

It seems likely that surplus gravel was transported by longshore drift to accumulate on Chesil Beach which thus operated as a sediment sink.

The hypothesis is supported by a variety of evidence. Surveys in Lyme Bay have failed to reveal alternative offshore shingle sinks. Chesil Beach is the closest shingle deposit of any size. No other significant shingle accumulations exist on the west Dorset or east Devon coast. Analysis of the size and lithology of cliff top gravels in the Charmouth area indicate that the material is comparable with Chesil Beach shingle. The size, shape and lithology of pebbles on Charmouth, Seatown, Eype and Chesil Beaches support the hypothesis that they were formerly connected. Contemporary littoral drift is eastward at Lyme Regis and Charmouth due to dominant drift during west and southwest storms. This situation probably existed over the last 5000 years unless coastal orientation was significantly different in the past and the frequency of west and southwest storms was reduced.

The present volume of Chesil Beach is estimated at 25 to 100 million tonnes (Carr, 1980). The estimated surplus supplied by coastal landsliding is 22 to 29 million tonnes ($1m^3$ = 1.6 tonnes) over the past 4000 to 5000 years. Although potential shingle supply from landslides is significant by comparison with the present volume of Chesil Beach, it is unlikely to have been the formative process. Chesil had already formed by 7000 years B.P. (Carr and Blackley, 1974). It is therefore suggested that sediment supply from terrestrial sources was a mechanism by which Chesil Beach has been nourished and enlarged. The original gravel source was probably fluvial and periglacial deposits on the floor of Lyme Bay, which gradually decreased in importance as the rate of sea level rise slowed down.

The fossil status of Chesil Beach may therefore be a recent phenomenon. Shingle supply from the west by littoral drift could have occurred as recently as the mid 1860's. Longshore transport was actually halted by the construction of two piers at West Bay. The supply process up to 1860 may have offset attrition losses and assisted in the maintenance of the unique Chesil Beach size grading (Carr, 1969) because it ensured that a wide range of pebble sizes was always available.

Conclusion

Sediment budget analysis indicates that protection afforded to the base of the sea cliff behind Seatown and Eype beaches is diminishing. Efficient shingle transport on the western part of Charmouth Beach is preventing accretion, despite rapid supply. The current trend for increasing coastal erosion is expected to continue in the future, particularly in view of recent predictions of accelerating sea level rise. Increased gravel supply at the coast due to landsliding will be transmitted eastwards, providing further accretion on the east part of Charmouth beach and increased supply to Seatown beach in the future. Boundaries to sediment transport systems are not always clearly defined, but may be variable. Such boundaries can be produced artificially, such as at West Bay. Others evolve naturally in a complex manner, such as at Golden Cap.

Studies of the coastal zone as a dynamic system, characterised by material inputs, stores, transfers and outputs, is a highly appropriate technique for coastal management. Alterations and variations in one part of the system are transmitted by feedback mechanisms, resulting in changes in other areas. The impact of human interference or systematic natural changes can therefore be assessed.

Access

The three pocket beaches are accessible at Charmouth (SY 365929), Seatown (SY 420916) and Eype Mouth (SY 448910). The transport boundary with the adjoining Chesil Beach can be viewed at West Bay (SY 462904). A car park is present at each locality. The Dorset Coast Footpath links all sites and generally follows the cliff-top between Charmouth and West Bay. Access is also possible along the foreshore but the sections beneath Golden Cap (SY 407923) and Doghouse Hill (SY 428913) should only be tackled at low water due to the danger of being cut-off by a rising tide.

Suggested route

Cars can be left in the municipal car park on the sea front at Charmouth (SY 366929) when visiting the first site (Figure 50). Walk along the beach either westward towards the foot of the Black Ven landslide complex (SY 355929) or eastward to the base of the cliffs beneath Stonebarrow Hill (SY 375927).

The potential for material supply at beach level is clearly evident from the boulder arcs marking previous positions of mudslide lobes at Black Ven and a combination of boulders and debris at the foot of Stonebarrow cliffs. The toe slope debris has either shunted over or fallen from the Lias cliffs. Observation of the truncated toes of mudslide lobes reveals much chert and flint gravel within a disturbed clay matrix. This material is derived from the landslide backscars and is the primary source for local shingle beaches and a potential source for Chesil Beach. Indeed, 80% to 90% of material currently being supplied to the beaches comes from the Black Ven and Stonebarrow landslides. On returning to the car park, a short walk along the coastal footpath up towards the summit of Stonebarrow Hill brings the Chert Beds deposit into view. This angular material becomes incorporated within the landslides, moves down to sea level during periods of instability and becomes part of the littoral zone sediment budget.

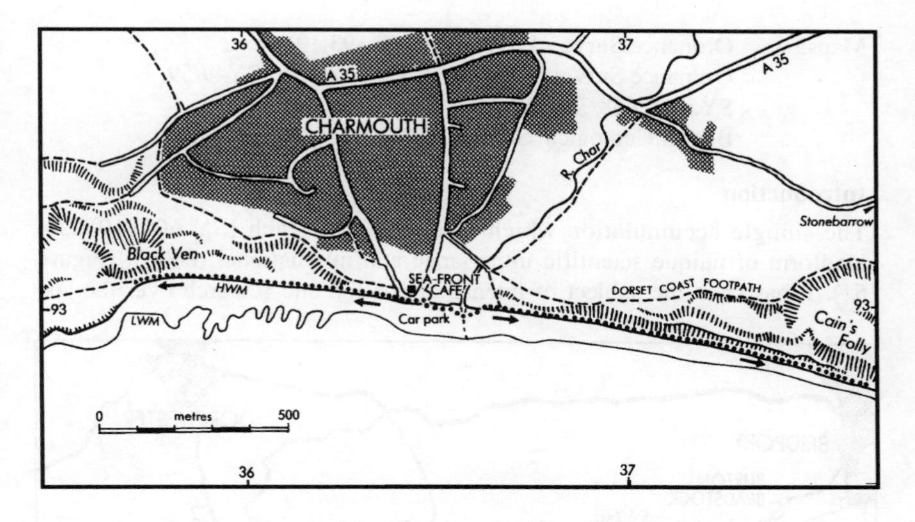

Figure 50. Suggested route for studying coastal sediment supply and transport.

CHESIL BEACH

Malcolm J. Bray

Maps: Ordnance Survey 1:50,000 sheets 193,194.
Ordnance Survey 1:25,000 sheets SY29/39, SY49/59, SY58, SY68/78, SY67/77.
British Geological Survey 1:50,000 sheets 327, 342.

Introduction

The shingle accumulation which forms Chesil Beach (SY 605810) is a landform of unique scientific importance and international renown (Figure 51). It has been the subject of intense discussion and research over the last

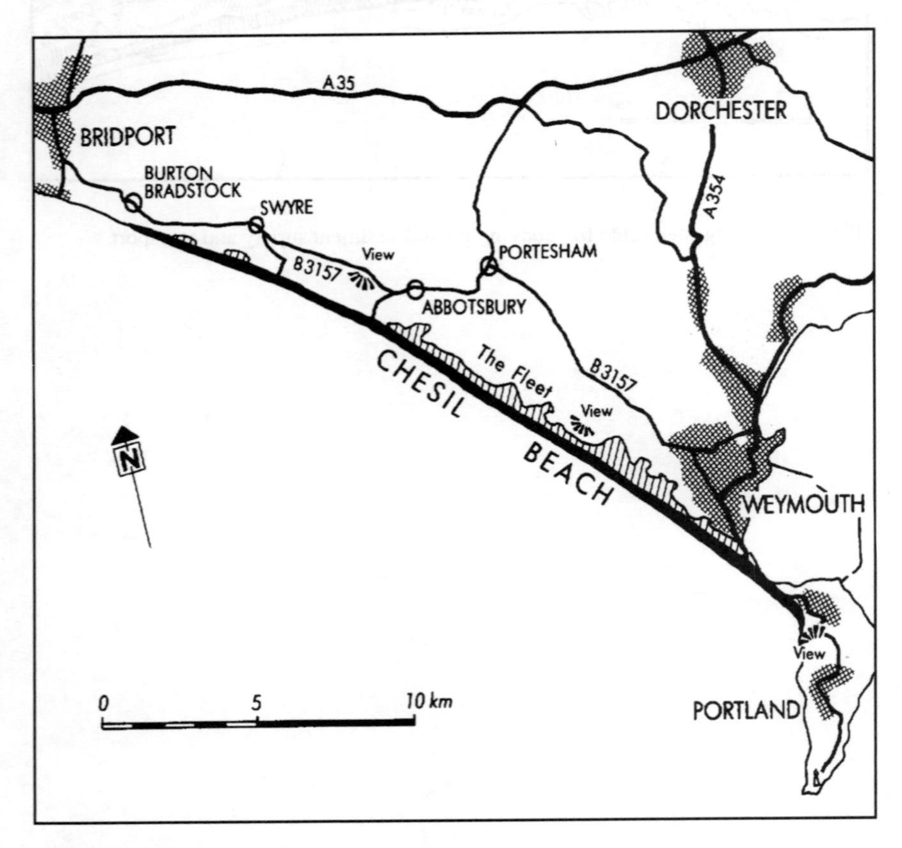

Figure 51. Chesil Beach.

150 years. The Beach also performs a critical coast protection and sea defence role but much concern has been expressed recently with regard to its continuing effectiveness in this function. Questions of origin, sediment source and contemporary dynamics are crucial to understanding its response to human pressures, such as gravel extraction, and natural changes, such as sea-level rise and storm variations (Figure 52).

Figure 52. The view west along Chesil Beach from the Isle of Portland.

Character of Chesil Beach

Chesil Beach is one of only three major shingle structures on the British coast and is distinctive in being a linear storm beach. The other two, Dungeness and Orford Ness, exhibit cuspate development. The piers at West Bay represent the present western terminus of Chesil Beach but prior to the change from open to closed pier structures in 1866, Eype Beach (SY 448910) to the west may also have been part of the same sediment transport system (Prior, 1919; Carr, 1980). Erosion to the west of West Bay following the construction of closed piers at the harbour mouth resulted in the setback of Eype Beach and probably separation from the Chesil Beach system (Jolliffe, 1979). In the east, the Beach terminates against the cliffs of the Isle of Portland. The shingle beach is joined to the mainland at the eastern and western ends but for 13km is backed by the shallow, tidal Fleet lagoon.

The visible pebble beach consists of about 98.5% chert and flint, the remainder being pink quartzite, quartz, locally derived limestone and occasional pebbles of igneous and metamorphic rocks (Carr and Blackley, 1969). The crest of Chesil is continuous over most of its length, although some irregularities occur in the Burton Bradstock area where the beach is backed by sandstone cliffs. Chesil generally increases in height from west to east, from an average of 6.0m O.D. to an average of 14.7m O.D. Beach face gradient also increases eastward, as does pebble size above low water mark, the size grading increasing systematically from West Bexington to Chiswell (Carr, 1969). Below low water mark, long-shore size grading is less evident, the shingle is coarser and less well sorted (Neate, 1967). On the basis of boreholes drilled through the beach down to bedrock (Carr and Blackley, 1973) beach shingle volume has been estimated at between 25 million and 100 million tonnes (Carr, 1980). The range of values reflects the uneven distribution of borehole information and uncertain shingle volume below low water mark due to shingle distribution in limited discontinuous horizons. More detailed descriptions of the beach are provided by Carr and Blackley (1974), Jolliffe (1979) and Carr (1980).

Sources of material and origin of the beach

Beach pebble lithology has led most authors to postulate a sediment source to the west from Devon (Fitzroy, 1853; Baden-Powell, 1930). Such theories implied that transport was eastward from the source areas by littoral drift along former shorelines (De La Beche, 1830; Coode, 1853; Rennie, 1853; Pengelly, 1870; Arkell, 1947) or offshore across Lyme Bay (Strahan, 1898). By contrast, Prestwich (1875) suggested north westward transport from a precursor of the Portland raised beach (SY 675684), situated south of the Isle of Portland. Prior (1919) suggested three possible sources. First, a precursor of Chesil stretching from Start Point in Devon to Portland. Second, erosion of the east Devon coast. Third, river gravels deposited in Lyme Bay by a previously extensive Fleet based river system. The latter possibility was supported by Bond (1951), who reconstructed an ancient Exe-Teign river, flowing eastward up to 10km offshore of the present coast, with a mouth southeast of Portland. Other possibilities, such as shingle rafting by ice, have also been suggested to account for pebbles of exotic lithology (Arkell, 1947).

By far the most comprehensive study of Chesil pebble lithology was undertaken by Carr and Blackley (1969), who concluded that all types could be related to either local sources or to existing sites in south-west England. The overriding opinion of previous work therefore supported the idea of supply to Chesil Beach from the west and a recent study suggests that terrestrial sources to the west may have been a major factor. Knowledge of Chesil Beach evolution remains incomplete, but the following chronological sequence has been compiled by Carr and Blackley (1973) and modified by Bray (1990).

The initial forerunner of Chesil probably existed as a bank well offshore of the present beach some 120,000 years ago. The bank was contemporaneous with the development of the Portland raised beach. During the last glacial, when sea-level was up to 130m lower than at present, a series of gravel rich deposits accumulated on what is now the floor of Lyme Bay. These probably comprised material from the Portland raised beach, solifluction deposits, river gravels and fluvio-glacial deposits laid down on the floor of Lyme Bay by meltwater at the end of the Devensian.

Formation of the present Chesil Beach began at the end of the Devensian, 20,000 to 14,000 years ago, when rapidly rising sea-levels caused erosion of gravel rich deposits and wave action drove the coarse materials on-shore as a barrier beach. Close to the land, the beach overrode existing sediments and The Fleet lagoon was rapidly filled with silt, sand, peat and pebbles. Dating of peat samples retrieved from boreholes suggests that infilling began about 7,000 years ago and was virtually complete by 5,000 B.P. Such deposition requires shelter, so a substantial barrier must have existed at this time, indication that Chesil Beach had formed at, or slightly seaward of its present position by 4,000 to 5,000 B.P. when sea-level approached its present elevation. Relict cliffs in abandoned in east Devon and west Dorset by falling sea-levels in the early Devensian were reactivated by marine erosion and supplied large quantities of gravel to the shore. Much of this material was transported to the east, where it nourished and enlarged the prototype Chesil Beach (Bray, 1990).

This evolutionary sequence suggests that Chesil initially formed mainly from pre-existing gravel deposits in Lyme Bay, which were swept on-shore as the beach migrated landwards and sea-level rose. The supply must have virtually ceased 4,000 to 5,000 years ago, when landward recession slowed. It appears that the beach continued to be nourished subsequently by terrestrial sources immediately to the west.

Sediment dynamics

Many previous accounts of Chesil Beach have suggested that the beach crest was lower in historic times, making breaching and overtopping more likely. This possibility was tested by the comparison of 1846-1853 profiles with those measured at corresponding positions in 1967-1969, 1978-1979 and

1990 (Carr and Gleason, 1972; Carr, 1983; Carr and Seaward, 1990). Results revealed that up to 1969, crest height has increased by an average 1.5m to 2.0m along western and central parts adjoining The Fleet but has fallen by up to 2.5m at Chesilton (SY 683735). A swell wave event of unusual wavelength and severity caused crest lowering by up to 2.5m at Chesilton on 13th February 1979. Subsequent recovery was intermittent and variable, with widespread lowering of the crest between Abbotsbury and Chesilton between 1969 and 1990. Studies involving profile measurements, photographic and documentary evidence indicate that only opposite Portland harbour was recession greater than the possible errors (Carr and Gleason, 1972). Furthermore, profile measurements following storms have revealed that short-term variations resulting from cut and fill cycles have been frequently greater than any long term trend (Gibbs, 1980). Available evidence therefore suggests that Chesil Beach continues to evolve slowly and that both crest height and plan shape are subject to intermittent variation with a tendency for lowering and slow recession respectively. However, it must be remembered that the period covered by accurate measurements is relatively short compared with the evolutionary time span of the beach and it is therefore difficult to conclusively establish long-term trends. It has been suggested that these changes may result from sea-level rise, variable storm climatology and the diminution of beach volume (Carr and Blackley, 1974).

Many theories have been presented to account for the unique long-shore size grading on Chesil Beach. Most theories attribute the grading to wave action, although several in the 19th century, now largely discredited, also considered tidal mechanisms (Barr and Blackley, 1974). Differential transport has been widely advocated, with large waves from the southwest (maximum fetch) transporting all pebble sizes to the east, while smaller waves from the southeast could only transport smaller pebbles back towards the west. The latter would almost certainly account for the considerable accumulation of fine shingle to the east of the east pier at West Bay. This pattern of movement was first proposed by De Luc (1811) and embellished by later authors to include concepts of sorting and abrasion. Preferential transport of larger pebble sizes in tracer experiments (Richardson, 1902; Jolliffe, 1964) led to the belief that pebble selection was associated with breaking wave height. However, the first detailed sedimentological and tracer studies indicated that pebble thickness was the critical parameter and that grading on the beach as a whole was unlikely to have a direct relation to breaking wave height (Carr, 1969 1971). Further studies revealed that pebble sorting was also related to wave frequency, the square root of significant wave height and the angle of swell approach (Gleason and Hardcastle, 1973). The unique long-shore size grading was therefore attributed to a complex interaction of factors arising from local sediment availability coupled with the incident wave climate but Carr and Blackley (1974) also identified the fossil nature of the beach as an important factor, arguing that fresh sediment inputs would tend to diminish size grading. Alternatively, some fresh input may be necessary to ensure availability of larger pebble sizes in the face of continuous reduction by attrition (Bray, 1990).

Problems in explaining the long-shore size grading along Chesil Beach can be attributed to incomplete understanding of littoral drift on Chesil Beach. Early tracer experiments using brickbats (Richardson, 1902) and painted pebbles (Adlam, 1961) showed net eastward transport governed by waves, which also caused preferential movement of larger material. These experiments were over very limited time periods so their results were in no way representative of long-term transport. More extensive and detailed experiments undertaken with pebbles of a foreign or exotic lithology confirmed the more rapid eastward transport of larger material (Carr, 1971). These experiments demonstrated marked eastward drift at Wyke Regis (SY 660760) but more variable and random movement near Portland. It was concluded, therefore, that there was no permanent drift near Portland, thereby accounting for the absence of a vast accumulation of pebbles at the eastern end. Whilst providing useful information relating to sorting processes, the overall patterns of drift recorded by these experiments were inconclusive because recoveries were low and unrepresentative of injected tracers and the experimental period was not representative of long-term conditions.

The marked trend for accretion on the eastern side of the West Bay piers provides strong evidence of net eastward drift at this western extremity of Chesil Beach (Hydraulics Research, 1979 1985; Jolliffe, 1979). Map comparisons and field survey covering 1901-1984 showed accretion was not continuous but interspersed with brief periods of erosion such as between 1961 and 1964 (Hydraulics Research, 1985). Littoral drift between Cogden Beach (SY 504880) and West Bay (SY 462904) was further studied by means of a mathematical beach model employing a representative wave climate derived from hindcasting, based on Portland wave data covering the period from 1974 to 1984 (Hydraulics Research, 1985). This study marked the first attempt to determine a reliable long-term estimate of drift on Chesil Beach and indicated mean net eastward transport at 8,000 $m^3 yr^{-1}$, which was validated by the documented trend for accretion against the east pier at West Bay. The accuracy of the analysis must be questioned, because it ignored swell waves and waves under one metre. Additionally, the shingle transport equations employed were calibrated on other beaches and therefore in need of further testing. Recent qualitative observations of beach erosion immediately east of the east pier at West Bay indicated possible changes in drift regime. Analysis of beach profiles and air photographs covering the period 1977 to 1990 revealed that the previously widely recognised trends for accretion ceased about 1982, whereupon a convincing switch to erosion resulted in mean high water level retreat of 40m by March 1990 (Hydraulics Research, 1991a). To explaining this change, wave climate and littoral drift were analyzed with techniques similar to those employed for the 1985 study (Hydraulics Research, 1991a). Wave climate was hindcast using Portland wind data covering the periods 1974 to 1990. Results showed that the wave climate changed remarkably after 1982, with fewer southeast storm waves and increased prevalence of westerly waves. Littoral drift calculations from this data revealed highly variable gross transport, with net westward drift before 1982 and a switch to net eastward drift of up to 14,000m^3yr^{-1} thereafter (Hydraulics Research, 1991a). These studies suggest that net littoral drift is very delicately balanced on Chesil Beach, so that slight wave climate / storm frequency variations can cause major drift reversals, thus linkages with adjoining systems are a distinct possibility. Available data covers too short a time span either to assess long-term trends or predict future behaviour. Beach morphometry is not a reliable guide because it may react relatively slowly to changes in drift regime due to large beach volume, so trends may only be recognisable at each end of the beach and will not contribute much towards an overall understanding.

Coast protection and sea defence

The Chesil Beach site is exposed and variable influenced by large waves generated in the Atlantic. Eastern parts are most exposed and comparison of wave records from West Bexington (SY 532865) and Wyke Regis (SY 660760) suggests that wave energy increases eastward along the beach (Hardcastle and King, 1972). Chesilton (SY 683735) is subject to periodic flooding during severe wave events and analysis by historical records and mathematical modelling reveal that two particular sizes of wave event cause problems. First, during strong, persistent onshore winds coincident with high tides, steep, short period storm waves may overtop the beach or percolate through it to cause flooding on the landward side. Analysis of this most common type of flood event identifies an extreme wave height of 6.5m for storm waves with a five year return period (Dobbie and Partners, 1980). The second event type comprises high, long period waves, generated in mid-Atlantic, transmitted up the English Channel and directed onto the eastern edge of the beach. An event of this type occurred in February 1979 and an offshore wave height of 9m was recorded. The crest of Chesil was overtopped and it can be postulated that this type of event may be a major factor in beach recession. Frequency of the event is undoubtedly low but difficult to determine due to scarcity of historical information and poor understanding of the formative meteorological conditions. Return periods of 50 years and 100 years or more were widely estimated by Dobbie and Partners (1980) and Draper and Bowass (1983) respectively.

Flooding is the greatest problem at Chesilton (Jolliffe, 1983) and following a number of particularly severe floods in the 1970's, the Wessex Water Authority initiated a sea defence scheme in 1980, costing an estimated £5 million. The scheme was completed in 1988 and involved trial beach stabilisation using gabion mattresses, modifications to the existing sea wall, a new intercepting drain landward of the crest and raising the level of the Weymouth road (Hooke and Kemble, 1991; Heinje and West, 1991). Flooding also occurs at West Bay (SY 462904), albeit less frequently (Jolliffe, 1979) than at Chesilton. Recent erosion of the east beach at West Bay has increased this possibility and a major beach nourishment scheme has been proposed (Hydraulics Research, 1991b).

Conclusions

It must be concluded that maintenance of Chesil Beach is essential from both scientific interest and coast protection viewpoints. Beach volume is recognised as the key issue (Figure 53). Studies have shown that Chesil Beach has been a fossil structure since at least 1866, when a transport boundary was created at West Bay, thereby cutting supply from the eroding coast to the west. Since then, minor gravel inputs from coast erosion and beach recession have been far outweighed by outputs by extraction and attrition (Bray, 1986 1990). In fact it is estimated that over 1.1 million tonnes of shingle were extracted between 1930 and 1977, somewhere between 1% and 4.5% of the total beach volume (Carr, 1980). Although the beach has suffered substantial depletion, the effects on profile and crest height are not easily determined due to high potential for shingle redistribution. With the cessation of all extraction by 1986, slow depletion resulting solely from attrition is now predicted. Recent measurements show variable but widespread lowering and recession of Chesil Beach crest between Abbotsbury (SY 577853) and Chiswell (SY 683735) over the period 1960 to 1990 (Carr and Seaward, 1990). Although these changes were directly related to two storms, beach gravel extraction losses may be an underlying contributory factor.

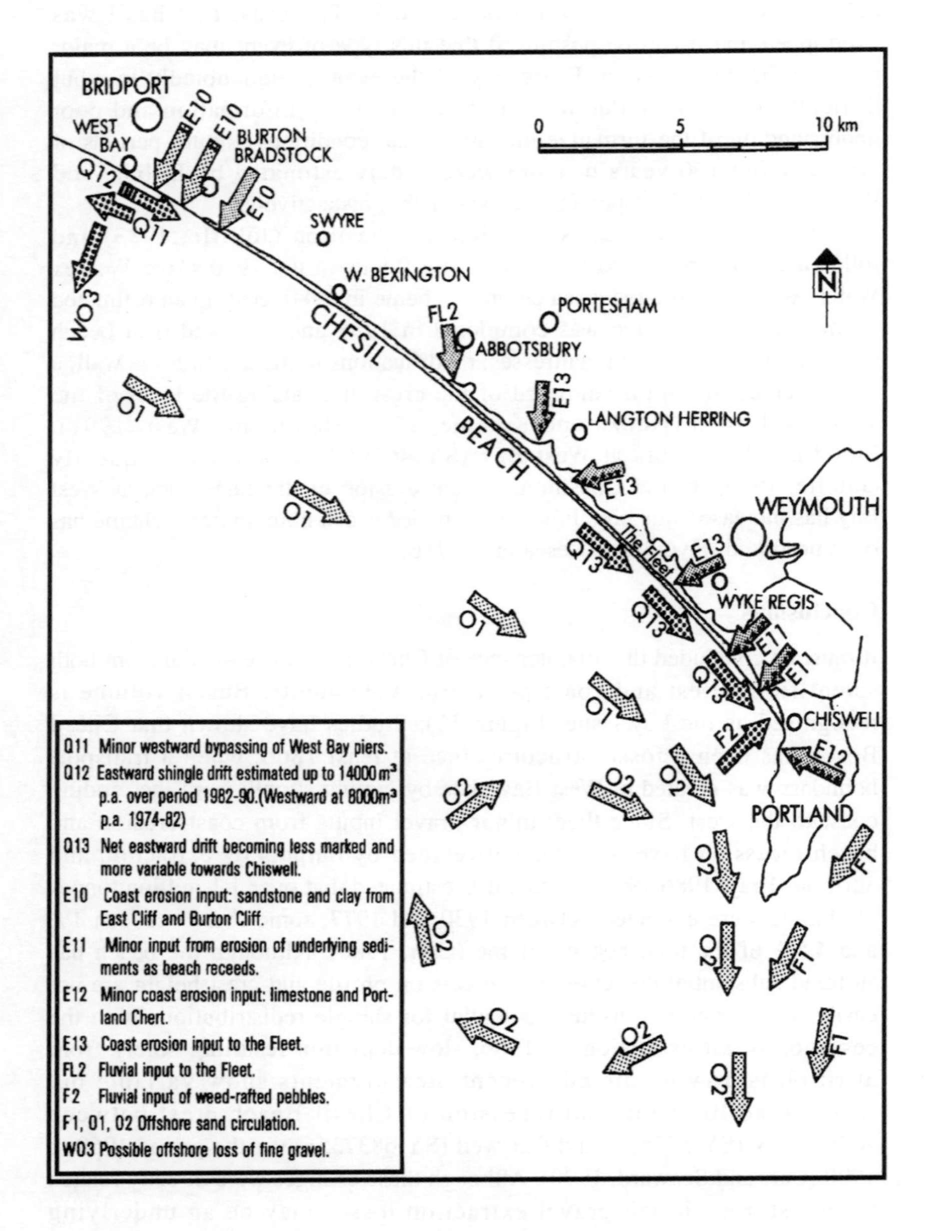

Figure 53. Sediment dynamics along Chesil Beach.

Reappraisal of Chesil Beach in the light of new information confirms its relict status, although this is probably a much more recent phenomenon than previously supposed. Transport from the eroding coast to the west could have supplied 14 to 18 million cubic metres of shingle over the last 4,000 to 5,000 years until the link was broken at West Bay harbour mouth in 1866. The beach must therefore be recognised as the major sink for coarse, durable products of coast erosion in west Dorset and east Devon over this period. These materials have been mixed with much larger quantities of gravel combed from the floor of Lyme Bay during the Holocene transgression and may have continued to nourish the beach as landward recession slowed 4,000 to 5,000 years ago.

It can be postulated that the survival and possible enlargement of the beach during the rapidly rising sea-level of the Holocene transgression can be attributed to continued shingle supply and a facility for landward recession. With current predictions of increased rates of sea-level rise and the potential for climatic change, Chesil Beach is entering a critical period in its evolution. Natural response mechanisms may be ineffective because the beach is now a finite resource and further landward recession is not possible at some locations due to adjacent cliffs and coast protection / sea defence requirements. Appropriate management responses may be necessary to carefully balance scientific interest against coastal protection.

Access

There are numerous points of access to Chesil Beach. On a clear day the best view of Chesil is from the car park on the summit of the north end of the Isle of Portland (SY 691731). The Beach can be seen stretching away to the west, with the high points of Thorncombe Beacon, Golden Cap and Stonebarrow Hill standing out on the distant horizon.

Good points to walk along the beach and examine the sediment size variation from east to west include Chiswell sea wall (SY 683735), the causeway which links Portland with the mainland (SY 670750), Abbotsbury (SY 577853), West Bexington (SY 532865), Cogden Beach (SY 504880), Burton Bradstock (SY 486896) and West Bay (SY 462904).

Suggested route

A car park is situated adjacent to the small harbour at West Bay (Figure 54). Walk down onto the beach on the east side of the harbour mouth. This is usually regarded as the start of Chesil Beach proper. Note the small size of the shingle that forms Chesil at this point. The cliffs which rise a short distance to the east of the harbour mouth are formed of Bridport Sands and are generally more resistant than the cliffs to the west. Nevertheless, the

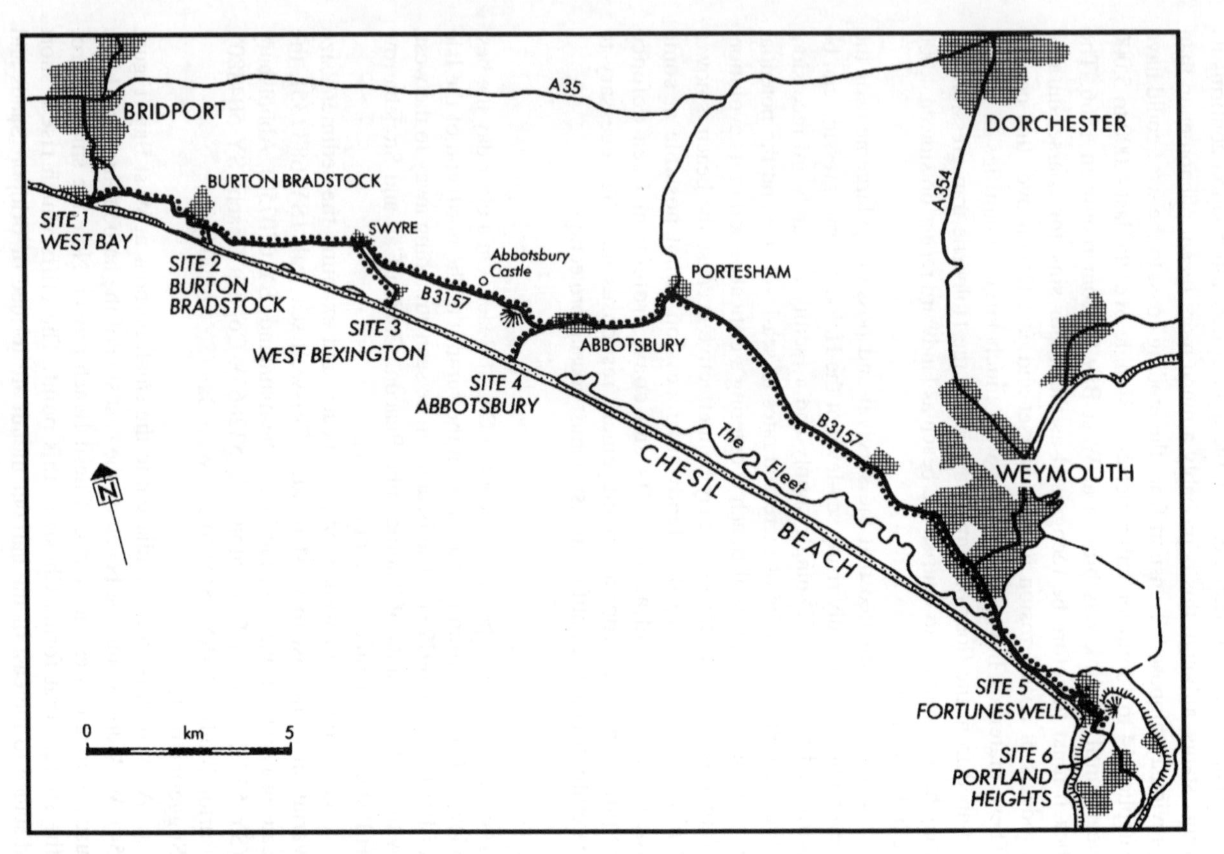

Figure 54. Suggested route for studying Chesil Beach.

erosion of East Cliff supplies small quantities of sediment which temporarily contribute to the beach before being destroyed by attrition. A steep but obvious path rises a short distance to the top of the cliff and gives a good view of the West Bay harbour mouth sediment transport barrier and Eype Beach beyond. Accumulation is obvious to the east of the piers and erosion and coastal set-back has occurred to the west, thereby creating an effective sediment transport barrier.

From West Bay, Chesil Beach extends all the way to the Isle of Portland in the east. Other good locations for visiting the coast (all of which have car park facilities) to examine the gradual change in beach sediment characteristics are Burton Bradstock, West Bexington, Abbotsbury and on the causeway linking the Isle of Portland to the mainland.

Leave West Bay and join the B3175 coast road, travelling east. In Burton Bradstock (SY 486896) a small side road in the centre of the village is signposted to the beach. A car park is located adjacent to the sea. The road into West Bexington leaves the main road in the village of Swyre (SY 527883). A car park is again situated immediately behind the beach. At Abbotsbury, as the B3175 road drops down towards the village, a fine view of the western edge of Chesil stretches away into the distance (see rear cover). This is the point at which The Fleet lagoon starts and separates the shingle beach from the land behind it (Figure 55). At the foot of the hill, turn immediately right and drive down towards the coast past Abbotsbury Gardens on the left-hand side. A car park is situated at the end of the lane. Thee are two noticeable changes at this point. First, the beach crest is noticeably elevated and second, the beach material is gradually increasing in size.

The size increase is particularly clear on the causeway which links Weymouth to Portland. This penultimate site is reached by returning from the beach at Abbotsbury to the B3175 road and driving through the villages of Portesham and Chickerell, into Weymouth and out towards Fortunswell village on the north end of Portland using the A354 road. This is the eastern end of Chesil. The beach material is now cobble size and a number of remedial engineering measures have had to be taken to protect the houses immediately behind the beach from flooding and shingle which gets thrown up during winter storm conditions. Of particular interest are the stone filled, gabion baskets, designed to protect the beach crest and prevent erosion and over-topping by storm waves.

The best location for concluding the itinerary is far above the beach in a car park adjacent to the Portland Heights Hotel (SY 691731). On a fine day the view stretches all the way along Chesil. The western end of The Fleet should be visible at Abbotsbury. The keen eyed will also be able to pick out the cliffs of Bridport Sand at West Bay and the summits of Thorncombe Beacon, Golden Cap and Stonebarrow Hill. On the horizon, the coast curves around towards Lyme Regis and Axminster.

Figure 55. The view east along Chesil Beach from Abbotsbury. The sea is to the right of the picture and the Fleet lagoon is to the left.

REFERENCES

ADLAM, W.J. 1961. The origin and source of some of the features of Chesil Beach, Dorset. *Southern Geographer*, **2**, 1-8.

AGER, D.V. & SMITH, W.E. 1965. *The coast of southern Devon and Dorset between Branscombe and Burton Bradstock*. Geologists' Association, London, 21pp.

ALLEN, P. 1972. Wealden detrital tourmaline implications for northwest Europe. Quarterly *Journal Geological Society of London*, **128**, 273-284.

ALLISON, R.J. 1986. *Mass movement and coastal cliff development of the Isle of Purbeck*, Dorset. Unpublished Ph.D. thesis, University of London, 714pp.

ALLISON, R.J. and BRUNSDEN, D. 1990. Some mudslide movement patterns. *Earth Surface Processes and Landforms*, **15**, 297-311.

ANDERSON, F.W. 1967. Ostracods from the Weald clay of England. *Bulletin Geological Survey of Great Britain*, **27**, 237-269.

ANDERSON, F.W. and BAZLEY, R.A.B. 1971. The Purbeck Beds of the Weald (England). *Bulletin Geological Survey of Great Britain*, **34**, 1-138.

ARBER, M.A. 1941. The coastal landslips of west Dorset. *Proceedings Geologists Association*, **52**, 273-283.

ARBER, M.A. 1973. Landslips near Lyme Regis. *Proceedings Geologists Association*, **84**, 121-133.

ARKELL, W.J. 1936. The tectonics of the Purbeck and Ridgeway faults in Dorset. *Geological Magazine*, **73**, 56-73 & 97-118.

ARKELL, W.J. 1947. *The geology of the country around Weymouth, Swanage, Corfe and Lulworth*. Memoirs of the Geological Survey of Great Britain. HMSO, London, 385pp.

BADEN-POWELL, D. 1930. On the geological evolution of Chesil Bank. *Geological Magazine*, **67**, 499-513.

BIRD, E.C.F. 1989. The beaches of Lyme Bay. *Proceedings Dorset Natural History and Archaeology Society*, **111**, 91-97.

BISHOP, A.W. 1973. The stability of tips and spoil heaps. *Quarterly Journal of Engineering Geology*, **6**, 335-376.

BOND, W.R.G. 1951. Theories as to the origin of Chesil Beach. *Proceedings Dorset Natural History and Archaeology Society*, **73**, 163-170.

BRAY, M.J. 1986. *A geomorphological investigation of the south west Dorset coast. Volume one: patterns of sediment supply*. Report to Dorset County Council, 144pp.

BRAY, M.J. 1990. *A geomorphological investigation of the south west Dorset coast. Volume two: patterns of sediment transport*. Report to Dorset County Council, 798pp.

BROMHEAD, E.N. 1986. *The stability of slopes*. Surrey University Press, Guildford, 373pp.

BROOK, D. 1991. Planning aspects of slopes in Britain. In: *Slope Stability - Engineering Developments and Applications*. Thomas Telford, London, 69-77.

BRUNSDEN, D. 1969. The moving cliffs of Black Ven. *Geographical Magazine*, **41**, 372- 374.

BRUNSDEN, D. 1973. The application of systems theory to the study of mass movement. *Geologica Applicata e Idrogeologia*, **8**, 185-207.

BRUNSDEN, D. 1974. The degradation of a coastal slope, Dorset, England. *Institute of British Geographers Special Publication*, **7**, 79-98.

BRUNSDEN, D. 1984. Mudslides. *In:* BRUNSDEN, D. and PRIOR, D.B. (Eds). *Slope Instability*. Wiley, Chichester, 363-418.

BRUNSDEN, D. and GOUDIE, A.S. 1981. *Classic coastal landforms of Dorset*. The Geographical Association, Sheffield, 20pp.

BRUNSDEN, D. and JONES, D.K.C. 1972. The morphology of degraded landslide slopes south west Dorset. *Quarterly Journal of Engineering Geology*, **5**, 205-222.

BRUNSDEN, D. and JONES, D.K.C. 1976. The evolution of landslide slopes in Dorset. *Philosophical Transactions Royal Society of London*, **283A**, 605-631.

BRUNSDEN, D. and JONES, D.K.C. 1980. Relative time scales and formative events in coastal landslide systems. *Zeitschrift fur Geomorphology*, **34**, 1-19.

CARR, A.P. 1969. Size grading along a pebble beach: Chesil Beach, England. *Journal of Sedimentary Petrology*, **39**, 297-311.

CARR, A.P. 1971. Experiments on longshore transport and sorting of pebbles: Chesil Beach, England. *Journal of Sedimentary Petrology*, **41**, 1084-1104.

CARR, A.P. 1980. *Chesil Beach and the adjacent area: outline of existing data and suggestions for future research.* Institute of Oceanographic Sciences Report to Dorset County Council and Wessex Water Authority, 21pp.

CARR, A.P. 1983. Chesil Beach: environmental, economic and sociological pressures. *Geographical Journal*, **54**, 53-62.

CARR, A.P. and BLACKLEY, M.W.L. 1969. The geological composition of the pebbles of Chesil Beach, Dorset. *Proceedings Dorset Natural History and Archaeology Society*, **90**, 133-140.

CARR, A.P. and BLACKLEY, M.W.L. 1973. Investigations bearing on the age and development of Chesil Beach, Dorset and the associated area. *Transactions Institute of British Geographers*, **58**, 99-111.

CARR, A.P. and BLACKLEY, M.W.L. 1974. Ideas on the origin and development of Chesil Beach, Dorset. *Proceedings Dorset Natural History and Archaeology Society*, **95**, 9-17.

CARR, A.P. and GLEASON, R. 1972. Chesil Beach, Dorset and the cartographic evidence of Sir John Coode. *Proceedings Dorset Natural History and Archaeology Society*, **94**, 125-131.

CARR, A.P. and SEAWARD, D.R. 1990. Chesil Beach: changes in crest height 1965- 1990. *Proceedings Dorset Natural History and Archaeology Society*, **112**, 109-112.

CASEY, R. 1961. The stratigraphical palaeontology of the Lower Greensand. *Palaeontology*, **3**, 487-621.

CASEY, R. 1963. The dawn of the Cretaceous period in Britain. *Bulletin South Eastern Union Scientific Societies*, **117**, 15.

CASEY, R. 1973. The ammonite succession at the Jurassic - Cretaceous boundary in eastern England. In: CASEY, R. and RAWSON, P.F. (Eds). *The Boreal Lower Cretaceous, Special Issue of the Geological Journal.* Seel House Press, Liverpool, 139-266.

CHATWIN, C.P. 1960. *The Hampshire Basin and Adjoining Areas.* HMSO, London, 99pp.

CONWAY, B.W. 1974. *The Black Ven landslip, Charmouth, Dorset.* Institute of Geological Sciences Report No.74/3. HMSO, London, 15pp.

CONWAY, B.W. 1979. The contribution made to cliff stability by Head deposits in the west Dorset coastal area. *Quarterly Journal of Engineering Geology*, **12**, 267- 275.

COODE, J. 1853. Description of Chesil Bank, with remarks upon its origin, the causes which have contributed to its formation and upon the movement of shingle generally. *Minutes of Proceedings Institute of Civil Engineers*, **12**, 520-557.

COPE, J.C.W. 1978. The ammonite faunas and stratigraphy of the upper part of the Kimmeridge Clay of Dorset. *Palaeontology*, **21**, 469-533.

DAVIES, D.K. 1967. Origin of friable sandstone-calcareous sandstone rhythms in the Upper Lias of England. *Journal of Sedimentary Petrology*, **37**, 1170-1188.

DAVIES, D.K. 1969. Shelf sedimentation: an example from the Jurassic of Britain. *Journal of Sedimentary Petrology*, **39**, 1344-1370.

DE FREITAS, M.H. and WATTERS, R.J. 1973. Some field examples of toppling failure. *Geotechnique*, **23**, 495-514.

DE LA BECHE, H.T. 1830. Notes on the formation of extensive conglomerate and gravel deposits. *Philosophical Magazine*, **2**, 161-171.

DE LUC, J.A. 1811. *Chesil tour dating from 1804*. Geological Travels Volume 2, London.

DENNESS, B. 1971. *The reservoir principle of mass movement*. Institute of Geological Sciences Report No.72/7, HMSO, London, 13pp.

DENNESS, B., CONWAY, B.W., McCANN,D.M. and GRAINGER, P. 1975. Investigation of a coastal landslip at Charmouth, Dorset. *Quarterly Journal of Engineering Geology*, **8**, 119-140.

DEPARTMENT OF THE ENVIRONMENT. 1990. *Planning policy guidance: development on unstable land*. HMSO, London, 14pp.

DOBBIE & PARTNERS. 1980. *Chesil sea defence scheme: synopsis of report*. Report to Wessex Water Authority and Weymouth and Portland Borough Council, 15pp.

DRAPER, L. and BOWNASS, T.M. 1983. Wave devastation behind Chesil Beach. *Weather*, **38**, 346-352.

FISCHER, A. 1856. On the Purbeck strata of Dorsetshire. *Transactions Cambridge Philosophical Society*, **9**, 555-581.

FITZROY, R. 1853. Discussion of COODE, J. Description of Chesil Bank, with remarks upon its origin, the causes which have contributed to its formation and upon the movement of shingle generally. *Minutes of Proceedings Institute of Civil Engineers*, **12**, 520-557.

GIBBS, P. 1980. Observations of short-term profile changes on Chesil Beach, Dorset. *Proceedings Dorset Natural History and Archaeology Society*, **102**, 77-82.

GLEASON, R. and HARDCASTLE, P.J. 1973. The significance of wave parameters in the sorting of beach pebbles. *Estuarine and Coastal Marine Science*, **1**, 11-18.

GREEN, C.P. 1969. An early Tertiary surface in Wiltshire. *Transactions Institute of British Geographers*, **47**, 61-72.

GREEN, C.P. 1974. The summit surface on the Wessex Chalk. In: BROWN, E.H. and WATERS, R.H. (Eds.). *Progress in Geomorphology*, Institute of British Geographers Special Publication No.7, London, 127-138.

GREEN, C.P. 1985. Pre-Quaternary weathering residues, sediments and landform development: examples from southern Britain. *In:* RICHARDS, K.S., ARNETT, R.R. and ELLIS, S. (Eds.). *Geomorphology and Soils*, Allen & Unwin, London, 58- 77.

HALLAM, A. 1964. Origin of the limestone-shale rhythms in the Blue Lias of England: a composite theory. *Journal of Geology*, **72**, 157-169.

HANSEN, M.J. 1984. Strategies for classification of landslides. *In:* BRUNSDEN, D. and PRIOR, D.B. (Eds). *Slope Instability*. Wiley, Chichester, 1-25.

HARDCASTLE, P.J. and KING, A.C. 1972. Chesil Beach sea wave records. *Civil Engineering and Public Works Review*, **67**, 299-300.

HAWKINS, J.B. 1991. Instability of Cobb Road, Lyme Regis, Dorset. In: *Slope Stability - Engineering Developments and Applications*. Thomas Telford, London, 115-120.

HEIJNE, I.S. and WEST, G.M. 1991. Chesil Sea Defence Scheme. Paper 2: Design of interceptor drain. *Proceedings Institution of Civil Engineers Part 1*, **90**, 799-817.

HOEK, E. and BRAY, J.W. 1981. *Rock Slope Engineering*. Institute of Mining and Metallurgy, London, 358pp.

HOOK, B.J. and KEMBLE, J.R. 1991. Chesil Beach defence scheme. Paper 1: concept, design and construction. *Proceedings Institution of Civil Engineers*, **90**, 783-798.

HOUSE, M.J. 1989. *Geology of the Dorset Coast*. Geologists' Association, London, 162pp.

HUTCHINSON, J.N. 1967. The free degradation of London Clay cliffs. *Proceedings Geotechnical Conference, Oslo*, **1**, 113-118.

HUTCHINSON, J.N. 1968. Mass movement. In: FAIRBRIDGE, R.W. (Ed.). *Encyclopedia of Earth Sciences*. Reinhold, New York, 688-695.

HUTCHINSON, J.N. 1970. A coastal mudflow on the London Clay cliffs at Beltinge, North Kent. *Geotechnique*, **20**, 412-438.

HUTCHINSON, J.N. 1971. Field and laboratory studies of a fall in Upper Chalk cliffs at Joss Bay, Isle of Thanet. *In:* PARRY, R.H.G. (Ed.). *Stress Strain Behaviour of Soils*, Foulis, Henley-on-Thames, 692-706.

HUTCHINSON, J.N. 1983. A pattern in the incidence of major coastal mudslides. *Earth Surface Processes and Landforms*, **8**, 1-7.

HUTCHINSON, J.N. 1984. An influence line approach to the stabilisation of slopes by cuts and fills. *Canadian Geotechnical Journal*, **21**, 363-370.

HUTCHINSON, J.N. and BHANDARI, R.K. 1971. Undrained loading, a fundamental mechanism of mudslides and other mass movements. *Geotechnique*, **21**, 353-358.

HYDRAULICS RESEARCH. 1979. *West Bay, Bridport, Dorset: a sea defence and coast protection study*. Hydraulics Research Report No. EX863, 12pp.

HYDRAULICS RESEARCH. 1985. *West Bay Harbour. A numerical study of beach changes east of the harbour entrance*. Hydraulics Research Report No. EX1301, 33pp.

HYDRAULICS RESEARCH. 1991a. *West Bay Harbour: analysis of recent beach changes east of the harbour*. Hydraulics Research Report No. EX2272, 16pp.

HYDRAULICS RESEARCH. 1991b. *West Bay Bridport: a random wave physical model investigation*. Hydraulics Research Report No. EX2187, 53pp.

ISAAC, K.P. 1979. Tertiary silcretes of the Sidmouth area, east Devon. *Proceedings Ussher Society*, **4**, 341-354.

ISAAC, K.P. 1981. Tertiary weathering profiles in the plateau deposits of east Devon. *Proceedings Geologists' Association*, **92**, 159-168.

ISAAC, K.P. 1983a. Silica diagenesis of Palaeogene kaolinitic residual deposits in Devon, England. *Proceedings Geologists' Association*, **94**, 181-186.

ISAAC, K.P. 1983b. Tertiary lateritic weathering in Devon, England and the Palaeogene continental environment of southwest England. *Proceedings Geologists' Association*, **94**, 105-115.

JOHNSON, A.M. 1970. *Physical Processes in Geology*. Freeman. San Francisco, 571pp.

JOLLIFFE, I.P. 1964. An experimental design to compare the relative rates of movement of different sizes of beach pebbles. *Proceedings Geologists' Association*, **75**, 67-86.

JOLLIFFE, I.P. 1979. *West Bay and the Chesil Bank, Dorset. Coastal regimen conditions, resource use and the possible environmental impact of mining activities on coastal erosion and flooding*. Report to West Dorset District Council, Dorset County Council, 87pp.

JOLLIFFE, I.P. 1983. Coastal erosion and flood abatement: what are the options? *Geographical Journal*, **149**, 62-67.

JONES, D.G. and WILLIAMS, A.T. 1991. Statistical analysis of factors influencing cliff erosion along a section of the west Wales coast, U.K. *Earth Surface Processes and Landforms*, **16**, 95-111.

JONES, D.K.C. 1980. The Tertiary evolution of southeast England with particular reference to the Weald. In: JONES, D.K.C. (Ed.). *The Shaping of Southern England*, Academic Press, London, 13-47.

JONES, D.K.C. 1981. *The Geomorphology of the British Isles: southeast and southern England*. Methuen, London, 332pp.

SMALL, R.J. 1980. The Tertiary geomorphological evolution of southeast England: an alternative interpretation. In: JONES, D.K.C. (Ed.). *The Shaping of Southern England*. Academic Press, London, 49-70.

JONES, M.E., ALLISON, R.J. and GILLIGAN, J. 1983. On the relationships between geology and costal landforms in central southern England. *Proceedings Dorset Natural History Archaeology Society*, **106**, 107-118.

KENNEDY, W.J. and GARRISON, R.E. 1975. Morphology and genesis of modular Chalks and hardgrounds in the Upper Cretaceous of southern Europe. *Sedimentology*, **22**, 311-386.

LANG, W.D. 1907. The Seltomian of Stonebarrow Cliff, Charmouth. *Geological Magazine*, **5**, 150-156.

LANG, W.D 1926. The Black Marl of Black Ven and Stonebarrow in the Lias of the Dorset coast. *Quarterly Journal Geological Society of London*, **82**, 144-165.

LANG, W.D. 1928. Landslips in Dorset. *Natural History Magazine*, **1**, 201-209.

LANG, W.D. 1936. The Green Ammonite Beds of the Dorset Lias. *Quarterly Journal of the Geological Society of London*, **92**, 423-437.

LANG, W.D. 1942. Geological Notes. *Proceedings Dorset Natural History and Archaeology Society*, **64**, 129-130.

LANG, W.D. 1944. Geological Notes. *Proceedings Dorset Natural History and Archaeology Society,* **66**, 129.

LANG, W.D. 1959. Report on Dorset natural history for 1958 - Geology. *Proceedings Dorset Natural History and Archaeology Society*, **80**, 22.

LANG, W.D. and SPATH, L.F. 1926. The Black Marl of Black Ven and Stonebarrow in the Lias of the Dorset coast. *Quarterly Journal Geological Society of London*, **82**, 144-187.

LANG, W.D., SPATH, L.F., COX, L.R. and MUIR-WOOD, H.M. 1928. The Belemnite Marls of Charmouth, a series in the Lias of the Dorset coast. *Quarterly Journal Geological Society of London*, **84**, 179-257.

LEE, E.M., MOORE, R., BRUNSDEN, D. and SIDDLE, H.J. 1991. The assessment of ground behaviour at Ventnor, Isle of Wight. In: *Slope Stability - Engineering Developments and Applications*. Thomas Telford, London, 189-194.

LEE, E.M., MOORE, R., BURT, N. and BRUNSDEN, D. 1991. Strategies for managing the landslide complex at Ventnor, Isle of Wight. In: *Slope Stability - Engineering Developments and Applications*. Thomas Telford, London, 201-206.

MELVILLE, R.V. and FRESHNEY, E.C. 1982. *The Hampshire Basin and adjoining areas*. HMSO, London, 146pp.

MINISTRY OF HOUSING AND LOCAL GOVERNMENT. 1961. *Town and Country Planning Acts 1947-1959: surface developments in coal mining areas*. HMSO, London.

MOORE, R.M. 1988. *The clay mineralogy, weathering and mudslide behaviour of coastal cliffs*. Unpublished Ph.D. thesis, University of London, 672pp.

MOORE, R., LEE, E.M. and LONGMAN, F. 1991. The impact, causes and management of landsliding at Luccombe, Isle of Wight. In: *Slope Stability - Engineering Developments and Applications*. Thomas Telford, London, 207-212.

NEATE, D.J.M. 1967. Underwater pebble grading of Chesil Bank. *Proceedings Geologists' Association*, **78**, 419-426.

PALMER, C.P. 1972. Revision of the zonal classification of the Lower Lias of the Dorset coast. *Proceedings Dorset Natural History and Archaeology Society*, **93**, 102- 116.

PALMER, M.J. 1991. Ground movements of the Encombe landslip at Sandgate, Kent. In: *Slope Stability - Engineering Developments and Applications*. Thomas Telford, London, 271-276.

PARSONS, C.F. 1976. A stratigraphic revision of the *humphriesianum subfurcatum* zone rocks (Bajocian Stage, Middle Jurassic) of southern England. *Newsletter Stratigraphy* **5**, 114-142.

PENGELLY, W. 1870. Modern and ancient beaches of Portland. *Reproduced and Transactions Devonshire Association Advanced Science*, **4**, 195-205.

PITTS, J. 1979. Discussion of: The contribution made to cliff instability by Head deposits in the west Dorset coastal area. *Quarterly Journal of Engineering Geology*, **12**, 277-279.

PITTS, J. 1981a. *Landslips of the Axmouth - Lyme Regis National Nature Reserve, Devon*. Unpublished PhD thesis, University of London, 710pp.

PITTS, J. 1981b. An historical survey of the landslips of the Axmouth - Lyme Regis Undercliffs, Devon. *Proceedings Dorset Natural History and Archaeology Society*, **103**, 101-105.

PITTS, J. 1983a. The temporal and spatial development of landslides in the Axmouth - Lyme Regis undercliffs National Nature Reserve. *Earth Surface Processes and Landforms*, **8**, 589-604.

PITTS, J. 1983b. The recent evolution of landsliding in the Axmouth - Lyme Regis undercliffs National Nature Reserve. *Proceedings Dorset Natural History and Archaeology Society*, **105**, 119-125

PRESTWICH, J. 1875. On the origin of the Chesil Bank and on the relationship of the existing beaches to past geological changes independent of the present coastal action. *Proceedings Institute of Civil Engineers*, **40**, 61-114.

PRIOR, D.B. and STEVENS, N. 1971. Some movement patterns of temperate mudflows, examples from north east Ireland. *Geological Society of America Bulletin*, **83**, 2533-2544.

PRIOR, E.S. 1919. The Bridport shingle. A discussion of pebbles. *Proceedings Dorset Natural History and Antiquarian Field Club*, **40**, 52-65.

RENNIE, J. 1853. Discussion of COODE, J. Description of Chesil Bank, with remarks upon its origin, the causes which have contributed to its formation and upon the movement of shingle generally. *Minutes of Proceedings Institute of Civil Engineers*, **12**, 520-557.

RICHARDS, K.S. and LORRIMAN, N.R. 1987. Basal erosion and mass movement. In: ANDERSON, M.G. and RICHARDS, K.S. (Eds). *Slope Stability*. Wiley, Chichester, 331-357.

RICHARDSON, L. 1928. The Inferior Oolite and contiguous deposits of the Burton Bradstock - Broadwindsor district, Dorset. *Proceedings Cotteswold Naturalists Field Club*, **23**, 35-68, 149-185 & 253-264.

RICHARDSON, N.M. 1902. An experiment on the movements of a load of brickbats deposited on Chesil Beach. Proceedings *Dorset Natural History and Antiquarian Field Club*, **23**, 123-133.

SELBY, M.J. 1982. *Hillslope Materials and Processes*. Oxford University Press, Oxford, 264pp.

SKEMPTON, A.W. and HUTCHINSON, J.N. 1969. *Stability of natural slopes and embankment foundations*. Proceedings 7th International Conference Soil Mechanics, State of the Art Volume, 291-340.

STONELEY, R. and SELLEY, R.C. 1986. *A field guide to the petroleum geology of the Wessex Basin*. R.C. Selley & Co. Ltd., London, 43pp.

STRAHAN, A. 1989. *The geology of the Isle of Purbeck and Weymouth*. Memoir of the Geological Survey of Great Britain. HMSO. London, 278pp.

SUMMERFIELD, M.A. and GOUDIE, A.S. 1980. The sarsens of southern England: their palaeo-environmental interpretation with reference to other silcretes. In: JONES, D.K.C. (Ed.). *The Shaping of Southern England*. Academic Press, London, 71-100.

TALBOT, M.R. 1973. Major sedimentary cycles in the Corallian Beds (Oxfordian of southern England). *Palaeogeography, Palaeoclimatology, Palaeoecology*, **14**, 293-317.

TORRENS, H.S. 1969. *International Field Symposium on the British Jurassic, Excursion No.1, Guide for Dorset and South Somerset*. University of Keele, 71pp.

TOWNSON, W.G. 1975. Lithostratigraphy and deposition of the type Portlandian. *Quarterly Journal Geological Society of London*, **131**, 245-272.

VARNES, D.J. 1978. Landslide types and processes. In: SCHUSTER, R.L. and KRIZEK, E.B. (Eds). *Landslides and their Control*. United States Transportation Research Board Special Report No.176. Transportation Research Board, Washington, 11-33.

WATERS, R.S. 1960. The bearing of superficial deposits on the age and origin of the upland plain of east Devon, west Dorset and south Somerset. *Transactions Institute of British Geographers*, **28**, 89-97.

WEBSTER, T. 1826. Observations on the Purbeck and Portland Beds. *Transactions of the Geological Society*, **2**, 37-44.

WHALLEY, W.B. 1984. Rockfalls. *In:* BRUNSDEN, D. and PRIOR, D.B. (Eds). *Slope Instability*. Wiley, Chichester, 217-256.

WILSON, V., WELCH, F.B.A., ROBBIE, J.A. and GREEN, G.W. 1958. *Geology of the country around Bridport and Yeovil*. HMSO, London, 239pp.

WIMBLEDON, W.A. and COPE, J.C.W. 1978. The ammonite faunas of the English Portland Beds and the zones of the Portlandian Stage. *Quarterly Journal Geological Society of London*, **125**, 183-190.

WOODWARD, H.B. 1885. *Rate of erosion of the sea coasts of England and Wales: Axmouth to Eype*. British Association for the Advancement of Science Report No.3, 423- 425.

GLOSSARY

Boulder arc

A line of boulders which mark a former position of the front edge of a mudslide toe lobe. The remnant boulders usually lie on a parabola and are often associated with past mudslide surges, where landslide material has moved out and away from the foot of a cliff. In west Dorset, boulder arcs are usually found on the beach below active mudslides, between the mean high water and mean low water lines.

Cohesion

A term describing the shear strength of a soil or rock under zero normal stress. In other words, cohesion is an indication of the bonds between particles in the absence of external forces pushing the particles together. An example is the chemical cementing of rock and soil particles by carbonate, silica or iron oxide cements.

Cut and fill cycles

Offshore sediment transport from the beach ridge to the near shore zone is characteristic of storm wave conditions and causes flattening (cut) of the beach profile. During swell wave conditions, sediment is moved onshore, causing beach ridge growth and steepening (fill) of the beach profile. Cut and fill cycles thus refer to short term fluctuations in beach profile.

Calabrian

A stratigraphical term in common use in the Mediterranean region until recently. Its stratigraphical usage has not been consistent but most often has referred to the Lower Quaternary. The term was employed by Wooldridge and Linton and by others since for unconsolidated deposits, possibly of marine origin, in southern England and of upper Pliocene or lower Pleistocene age.

Cryoturbation

Contortions of bedding in superficial deposits caused by ground freezing and / or the thawing of ground ice.

Duricrust

Hard layers consisting of concentrates of aluminous, siliceous, ferruginous or calcareous materials found capping the ground surface or within the uppermost parts of a weathering profile. The chemical composition depends on the substratum which is strongly leached. They are most characteristic of areas of low relief and are mainly Cenozoic in age.

Extensometer

A device for measuring the rate of movement in landslides. Extensometers can be mechanical or electronic in operation and record when slip takes place at a specific point on the surface of a mudslide.

Friction angle

Friction is the basic control on the strength of soil and rock materials where particles are in contact with each other. The friction angle is the critical angle for a given set of material properties, which separates stable conditions on the one and unstable conditions on the other. In other words, if a mudrock has a friction angle of 24°, slopes in the material with a mean angle at or close to 24° will be potentially unstable. Slopes with a mean angle well below 24° will be less likely to fail. Friction angle is a parameter usually determined in the laboratory using apparatus such as a shear box or triaxial cell.

Graben

A valley, trough or depression produced by processes such as faulting, subsidence or landsliding.

Gelifluction

The creep or flow of thawed material over frozen sub-surface layers. The term is preferred to solifluction since the latter does not necessarily imply the existence of a cold climate.

Holocene (Flandrian) transgression

Global sea-level rise caused by melting ice sheets at the end of the recent Devensian glacial period. Although variable across the globe, the Holocene Transgression is thought to have covered the period 16,000 B.P. to 4,000 to 5,000 B.P. in Britain, involving sea-level rise of up to 100m.

Hydraulic conductivity

A term used to describe the physical properties of a fluid and the material through which it is flowing. Hydraulic conductivity reflects the ease with which a fluid passes through a porous material.

Inclinometer

Field apparatus used to measure internal distortions within a mass of moving material, usually between the base of a landslide and the ground surface.

Kaolinite

A hydrated silicate of alumina, produced principally by decomposition of feldspar by kaolinization. This process may take place either by prolonged sub-aerial weathering or by underground pneumatolysis (producing kaolin or china clay). At the surface or in the upper part of a weathering profile, induration can occur to produce duricrusted kaolinite (see duricrust).

Lateral shear

The boundary between a landslide and adjacent stable ground, or two landslides which are moving in juxtaposition. The lateral shear is the point where the shear surface of a landslide outcrops at the ground surface. Lateral shears usually appear as lines on the ground which can be traced around the perimeter of a landslide.

Laterite

A highly ferruginous weathering product, characteristic of humid or semi- humid tropical areas, usually red in colour and often highly indurated at the surface (see duricrust). High temperatures and a seasonally wet and dry climate aiding the mobilisation and downward leaching of silica are thought to be necessary.

Littoral drift

Wave powered sediment transport parallel to the coast. On shingle beaches this is generally by a mechanism generated by oblique incident waves.

Littoral zone

The zone extending seawards from the landward margin of the beach, into water to a depth at which wave powered sediment transport is limited.

Morphodynamic Zone

Geomorphological features, such as landslides, can frequently be sub-divided into sections. An example is mudslides which usually comprise a headward feeder or bowl, a track or zone of transport and a toe lobe. Such divisions are termed morphodynamic zones, representing units within geomorphological systems which help to explain interactions between processes and landforms.

Neotectonics

Crustal movements resulting in deformation of strata from the mid-Tertiary to the present.

Peak strength

The maximum strength of undisturbed rock or soil.

Periglacial

Describing a zone of variable width peripheral to present day or former glacial ice. Large areas of this zone are now, or were in the past, characterised by the presence of permafrost and / or ground ice. Climatic conditions in a periglacial zone range from severe cold to moderate cold, and from arid to humid. The commonest vegetation ranges from tundra to boreal forest.

Piezometer

A measuring device used in the field to monitor pore water pressure.

Pore water pressure

The pressure exerted by water in the pore spaces of a soil or sedimentary material. Pressure is positive when below the water table and negative when above the water table. Pore water pressure can be measured using a piezometer.

Pressure ridge

A ridge of material which develops when movement is occurring at different rates within a landslide. For a pressure ridge to form, material towards the top of a landslide moves faster than material lower down the slope. A 'shunting' effect occurs, with the sliding debris pushing up ridges of material.

Reidel shear

Small, curved, sinusoidal shears, which develop across lateral shears during periods of landslide movement due to friction effects between the stable and unstable ground.

Residual strength

The strength of a soil or rock following disturbance. Movement in a landslide, for example, will reorientate the mineral particles, reducing the strength of the material from its peak to its residual value.

Sarsen

Cenozoic silcretes found in Britain. Sarsens usually occur as separated blocks, no longer in situ. Frequently they have been moved by man or by natural processes such as gelifluction.

Silcrete

A duricrust consisting predominantly of siliceous material. An arbitrary limit of at least 85% SiO_2 is often adopted. A tropical or sub-tropical, arid to humid environment is required for silcrete formation.

Shear resistance

The resistance of a soil or rock to deformation and failure.

Shear strength

A measure of the ability of a material to resist deformation and failure. This is an important parameter which is fundamental in determining how a material behaves. Shear strength is influenced by a wide variety of parameters such as particle size, and pore water pressure.

Shear surface

The boundary of a landslide at its base and sides, marking the zone of movement and thus delimiting stable and unstable ground. The shear surface is sometimes referred to as the slip surface.

Slip surface

The boundary of a landslide at its base and sides, marking the zone of movement and thus delimiting stable and unstable ground. The slip surface is sometimes referred to as the shear surface.

Tension crack

A fissure which opens up in a landslide when rates of slip vary within an individual feature. For a tension crack to develop, material towards the toe of a landslide moves faster than material higher up the slope. A `stretching' effect occurs, with the sliding debris pulling apart, allowing fissures to open up.

Unconformity

A lack of continuity in deposition between strata in contact. The surface of unconformity marks a gap in the stratigraphic record, corresponding to a period of erosion or non-deposition.

Undercliff

An area of ground beneath a cliff. In Dorset the term refers to unstable ground below a cliff from which material intermittently becomes detached and loads the rear of the slope.

Visco-plastic flow

A type of movement characteristic of some landslides where the debris moves as a highly viscous material. Some mudslides exhibit visco-plastic flow.

Wave climate

The long term distribution of waves incident at a particular site, with respect to wave height, period and direction of approach.

NOTES

NOTES